ASE Guide to Primary Science Education

Edited by Rosemary Sherrington

STANLEY THORNES

Acknowledgements

Thanks go to the members of the ASE Publications committee and the Primary Science Committee for their support and invaluable comment, and Essex County Council for their permission to use the materials in Chapter 3.1. Special thanks go to the authors of the book, who contributed so willingly.

Published in 1998 by:
The Association for Science Education
College Lane
HATFIELD
AL10 9AA

Produced in 1998 for The Association for Science Education by:
Stanley Thornes (Publishers) Ltd
Ellenborough House
Wellington Street
CHELTENHAM
GL50 1YW

A catalogue record for this book is available from the British Library.

ISBN 0 86357 290 1

02 03 04 05 / 10 9 8 7 6 5 4

Typeset by Action Typesetting Ltd
Front cover designed by DHH Printing & Design
Printed and bound in Spain by Graphycems

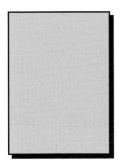

Contents

Introduction

This guide is for all those involved in teaching primary science. It will be of value to student teachers, those already experienced in teaching primary science and those with management responsibility for science in their school. Its terms of reference cover the age-range from pre-school to the end of Key Stage 2.

It is published in partnership with the *ASE Guide to Secondary Science Education*, with which it shares several chapters, and is intended to supplement and up-date the ASE Primary Science Handbook. The Guide aims to cover central and other, more diverse issues of primary science. There are threads and areas of contention which run through the book. The contributors are experienced practitioners and researchers; each brings an individual perspective and considerable expertise to the examination of an important issue within science education.

The issues discussed are important whatever the detail of the science curriculum being taught. Thus, it is expected that the principles in each chapter will be of value across the UK and internationally. However, it is inevitable that, in places, the discussion is in a particular *context* to illustrate the principles. This context is often related to practice in England and Wales, partly because it is the one most familiar to the writers. We hope you will be able to extend the principles to whatever context you are working in.

Whilst it is impossible to predict details of the future with any accuracy, we can be sure that science will play an important part in the curriculum. Primary science will provide the foundation for the advancements of future generations. Added to this, our knowledge and understanding of primary science education is not static, it will evolve as we learn more about its learning and teaching. This Guide offers an insight into current thinking, strategies and best practices to provide a philosophy and framework which will stand the test of time.

Science, together with literacy and numeracy, constitute the core of children's education. Why this is so is to do with the specific experiences involved in learning science and these are discussed at length throughout the Guide.

Section 1 – The Purposes of Science Education – aims to give an overview of the world of science education. The writers discuss such issues as, Why Teach Science? What are the characteristics of good science teaching? Where have we come from and where should we go? How can we open science fully to all children? How does our science curriculum compare to that of other countries? Many of these themes are developed further in the ensuing sections.

Section 2 – Learning Science – includes the development of scientific concepts and the skills of investigation, and discusses ways in which children can best learn them. Social and ethical considerations are increasingly important to our lives as a scientifically educated nation and this, together with links between subjects, environmental education and design and technology and with industry, widen the context for science learning.

In Section 3 – Teaching Science – the writers consider good classroom practice. Good teaching is at the heart of science. The chapters include planning a broad, progressive curriculum of sufficient depth, and planning lessons which bring the curriculum and the children together in well-targeted activities. There are suggestions for developing teaching techniques which challenge, entice and motivate through focused classroom interaction. Assessing children's progress through incisive insight into their understanding, and using IT to further learning, combine to bring to life the characteristics of good teaching described in earlier chapters.

The commentary before Section 4 highlights the importance of professional development for science teachers as an introduction to issues of management.

Finally, the writers of Section 4 – Managing Science – look at how good teaching should be supported by good management. The role of the subject leader has become increasingly important. The responsibilities include keeping up-to-date and knowing how to choose and use the available resources. Developing rigorous oversight of the science curriculum and insight into its teaching are relatively new aspects of the role. It is an increasingly important one in seeking to improve learning and in the professional development of teachers. Last, but not least, ways in which the findings of inspections can be used will help schools to take the initiative for their own continuous improvement.

Constant changes in curriculum, assessment and styles of learning are inevitable as we seek to improve children's education and teaching. We don't yet know the limits of learning. Who knows what children may achieve with the very best teaching?

Full details of ASE Policies referred to throughout the book are available on the ASE's website, along with other invaluable information and discussion: **http://www.ase.org.uk**

Rosemary Sherrington

August 1998

SECTION 1

The Purposes of Science Education

1.1 The Purposes of Science Education

Mary Ratcliffe

What are the purposes of science education? If you've given this question some thought it may be in the context of one of the following scenarios:

- As a classroom teacher, justifying the topic being studied; 'Why do we have to study this? It's boring.'
- As a primary science co-ordinator, dealing with colleagues; 'How am I going to teach science? It's difficult and I've managed my life perfectly well with little knowledge of science.'
- As a Head of Science, justifying curriculum structures and timetabling to school management; 'Why should science take such a significant part of the school curriculum?'
- As a pastoral tutor discussing career options with adolescents; 'Why should I study any science subject after I've left school?'

All these scenarios raise questions about:

- the place of science in a school curriculum
- the perceived nature of science and its constituent disciplines
- the nature and purposes of science education.

In this chapter I explore the nature of science and the purposes of science education.

What is science?

Is science:
- A collection of discrete disciplines – biology, chemistry, physics, astronomy, etc. – with clearly-defined bodies of knowledge?
- *The* method of exploring and extending knowledge about the world?
- Activities conducted by researchers in laboratories in extending and manipulating knowledge?

All these descriptions may be part of the picture but each is flawed in some respect. As soon as we try to pin down what we mean by 'science', different views and values come into play. The conduct of science is an activity --it is a human endeavour.

The Oxford English Dictionary(OED) has five 'definitions of science' reflecting the history of the word 'science' – coming from Old French and Latin 'to know' – through to the interpretation of science as an academic discipline in schools and universities.

The 1725 OED definition, reflects knowledge and processes:

A branch of study which is concerned with a connected body of demonstrated truths or with observed facts systematically classified and more or less bound together by being brought under general laws, and which includes trustworthy methods for the discovery of new truth within its own domain. (OED)

However, what is the knowledge base? Is science just 'biology, chemistry and physics'? (See Chapter 1.5 for a discussion of how different European countries view the content of science.) Science is generally viewed as knowledge about the natural and material world. The boundaries are not clear. Is, for example, psychology, pharmacy or biotechnology a science?

There is much written about the nature and purposes of science. I cannot do justice to a consideration of the differing perspectives on the nature of science. Useful reading is given at the end of the chapter. Here, it may be pertinent to consider whether there is a view of science expressed in national curricula. This might help in interpreting the purposes of 'school science'.

The Science National Curriculum orders in England and Wales currently lack a clearly-stated rationale both in terms of the nature of the discipline and of the purposes of science education (DfE, 1995). However, the original non-statutory guidance gives some indication of an underlying view of science:

Scientists are curious; they seek explanations. The scientist chooses from the knowledge and ideas which have been previously established to devise systematic studies into scientific phenomena. There are many scientific methods – scientists formulate hypotheses, design and carry out experiments, make observations and record results. There is also an important place for imagination, for inspirational thinking and the receptive mind. ...... A scientist's work can result in the formulation of a new idea or lead to the solution of a problem or the development of a new product. Scientific endeavour produces progressively more powerful ways of understanding the natural world. (NCC, 1989, p A4).

So far this seems reasonable and in line with other views of science. But what of the next bit:

The distinctive nature of science is that it relies more heavily on certain skills than do other areas of human enquiry. Making and testing of hypotheses by observation and experimentation are essential characteristics of science. Another distinction is its general area of interest. Science is a human construction. We define its boundaries and decide what shall count as a science.

Ah, so the jury's still out as to whether psychology, pharmacy and biotechnology are sciences?

Perhaps the most contentious part of this description of 'What it means to be scientific' is the final sentence:

School science is a reflection of science in the 'real' world, where scientists learn from each other and extend the boundaries of knowledge by research.

It would be interesting to know whether this is a consensus view of 'school science'. Do we really mirror the real world of research in science classrooms? Do pupils view themselves as explorers or as receivers of agreed scientific knowledge?

The Science Review Group of the Scottish Consultative Council on the Curriculum take an overarching view of the nature of science:

> ... *science is a distinctive form of creative human activity which involves one way of seeing, exploring and understanding reality.*
>
> *Science is not a homogeneous activity generating a single form of knowledge. On the contrary, there is a variety of distinguishable, but interconnected and overlapping disciplines within the scientific domain. All of these 'sciences' are concerned with investigating and understanding aspects of the natural and man-made world, albeit from different perspectives and with variations in the methods of enquiry used. The essential humanness of science is manifested in its modes of working, in its motivations and in the ways it affects and is affected by social and, cultural and historical contexts.* (Scottish CCC, 1996)

This has some similarity with NCC's views and that of some, but not all, philosophers of science. There is a variety of perspectives on the nature of science. Nott and Wellington (1993) provide a useful activity to explore your own views. They see a number of elements, with a continuum from one extreme to another, as contributing to an individual's perspective:

- Relativism vs. positivism – truth as being relative or absolute.
- Inductivism vs. deductivism – generalising from observations to general laws versus forming hypotheses and testing observable consequences.
- Contextualism vs. decontextualism – science interdependent with or independent of cultural context.
- Process vs. content – science characterised mainly by processes or by facts and ideas.
- Instrumentalism vs. realism – science as providing ideas which work versus a world independent of scientists' perceptions.

Exploration of the philosophy of science is needed by all teachers of science to ensure that they can articulate a clear perspective of their own. Too often, because we lack an exploration of the nature of science in our own education, our views on the nature of science and, therefore, its translation into school science are underdeveloped.

What is clear is that values are being transmitted in every science classroom, implicitly or explicitly. All school science education is imbued by values; even that which attempts to present scientific processes as uninfluenced by human characteristics. Pupils may be gaining a view of science as a creative, human endeavour influenced by cultures and beliefs or as a collection of objective, value-free facts. Science education which explores the nature of science may assist future generations in dealing with a scientific and technological society.

Relationship between Science and Technology

The boundaries between science and technology are blurred, particularly in everyday parlance. Note the 'Tomorrow's World' presenter who talks about the programme 'showing the latest in scientific development'. Yet the content of this popular television programme is mainly concerned with *technological* improvements – using existing scientific knowledge and not necessarily exposing cutting-edge research which extends our knowledge of the natural and material world. Similarly, the popular journal *New Scientist* deals with advances in both science and technology. This raises issues about the relationship between science and technology in the curriculum. Take 'genetic cloning' as an example. This depends on sound scientific knowledge, yet the breakthrough in producing clones comes with increasing technological improvement. It could be argued that science and technology are so closely linked that to separate them in the curriculum is not sensible. Are biotechnology and engineering sciences or technologies?

In Northern Ireland science and technology are integrated into common programmes of study in the primary curriculum, but remain separate in the rest of the UK. The holistic nature of the primary curriculum, however, can allow integration of science and technology even if there are separate programmes of study. (See Chapter 2.7.)

Layton (1993) argues that there is similarity between the design–make–evaluate technology process, a science problem-solving process and a general model of problem-solving. However, Layton also shows that the constraints surrounding the processes are different in a science and in a technology context. Technology might be argued to be 'customer and product' oriented whereas science is 'knowledge' oriented with far fewer constraints on its conduct.

Purposes of Science Education

To gain an appreciation of the underlying purposes of the Science National Curriculum, we could again refer to the non-statutory guidance. This offers the following as the contributions of science to the school curriculum:

> *1. Understanding the key concepts of science will allow pupils to use them in unfamiliar situations...*
> *2. Using scientific methods of investigation will help pupils to make successful, disciplined enquiries and use ideas to solve relevant problem...*
> *3. Appreciating the contributions science makes to society will encourage pupils to develop a sense of their responsibilities as members of society and the contributions they can make to it...*
> *4. Learning in science contributes to personal development...*
> *5. Appreciating the powerful but provisional nature of scientific knowledge and explanation will bring pupils closer to the process by which scientific models are created, tested and modified...*
> *6. Giving students access to careers in science and design and technology is vital...*
> (NCC, 1989, p A4)

In looking to the future, Scottish CCC suggests that:

For individual learners, experience of science education should:
– broaden understanding of themselves, human culture and societies and the
natural and made worlds in which they live;
– help to sustain natural human curiosity, develop an enquiring mind and
foster an interest in continuing to learn throughout life;
– help to engender a critical way of thinking about phenomena and issues;
– support other aspects of learning across the curriculum;
– develop the potential to contribute in an informed, thoughtful and sensitive
way to the enhancement of people's lives and of the environment. (Scottish
CCC, 1996)

The Science National Curriculum in Northern Ireland has the following in the introduction to the Programme of Study at Key Stage 3:

Pupils should consider the benefits and drawbacks of applying scientific and
technological ideas to themselves, industry, the environment and the community. They should begin to make personal decisions and judgements based on
their scientific knowledge of issues concerning personal health and well being,
safety and the care of the environment. Through this study, pupils should
begin to develop an understanding of how science shapes and influences the
quality of their lives.

All three of these descriptions bring in their respective underlying views of science and, importantly, the personal development of the pupil.

Some science educators have argued for science education as a grounding in 'scientific literacy' or for the 'public understanding of science'. The UK Curriculum Councils' descriptions of pupils' experiences have some similarity to the three strands of 'scientific literacy' agreed by the many commentators (e.g. AAAS, 1989; Driver *et al*, 1996; Millar, 1996). Pupils should gain:

• knowledge and understanding of some science concepts
• an understanding that scientific endeavours are social human activities, involving value judgements and cultural contexts
• an understanding of the processes involved in the conduct of and reasoning about science.

However, we still have to answer the question, Why do we consider these three strands so important in pupils' education? Millar (1996) groups the arguments for 'public understanding of science' into five categories:

a) Economic – there is a connection between the level of public understanding of science and the nation's wealth.
b) Utility – an understanding of science is useful practically in a technological society.
c) Democratic – an understanding of science is necessary to participate in decision-making about issues with a base in science.
d) Social – it is important to maintain links between science and the wider culture.
e) Cultural – science is the major achievement of our culture and all young people should be enabled to understand and appreciate it.

You might like to consider these arguments in the context of the scenarios at the start of the chapter or carry out the exercise suggested by Millar (1993) in an earlier version of this book. The cultural and democratic arguments are supported by the discussions of the Nuffield Foundation Seminar Series (Reports 1–3).

No simple slogan – 'scientific literacy', 'public understanding of science', 'citizen science'- can adequately convey how these strands interrelate. Fig 1.1A is one attempt to portray the elements contributing to 'scientific literacy'.

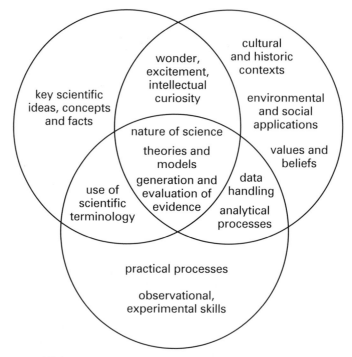

Fig 1.1A Elements of Science

This alone cannot constitute an adequate description of the purposes of science education. The development of the individual pupil is important. Fig 1.1B shows how the elements of 'scientific literacy' could contribute to pupils' personal development.

If any one of the areas in Figs 1.1A and 1.1B is missing, then the individual's education is impoverished. Equally, pupils can miss out if the purposes are skewed in any way through particular methods of curriculum interpretation. This can happen, for example, if acquisition of facts and concepts is emphasised at the expense of development of analytical skills.

Jenkins (1997a) recognises the individual in his discussions of 'functional' public understanding of science. He identifies significant features of an individual's approach to science in his discussion of 'citizen science' (Jenkins, 1997b):

a) *The interest of citizens in science and technology is differentiated by science, social group and gender.* Crudely, people may be more interested in medical matters than physical sciences – particularly females.

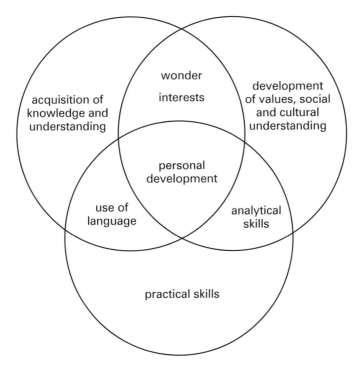

Fig 1.1B Education of the whole person

b) *For most citizens, interest in science and technology is linked with decision-making or action.* We may seek science knowledge for specific social purposes related to health, leisure and local decision-making.

c) *Citizens choose a level of explanation adequate for the purpose in hand.* We hold ideas about science concepts, some of which are misconceptions, which have proved adequate for everyday life.

d) *Citizens consider scientific and technological knowledge alongside other available knowledge.* During our personal, working and social lives, we construct a body of practical knowledge, tested and validated against individual and collective experience.

e) *Citizens consider scientific knowledge alongside its social and institutional connections.* We may ask questions about the source and validity of scientific knowledge, particularly if there are conflicting 'expert' views.

f) *Citizens have complex attitudes to risks associated with scientific or technological issues.* Risk is viewed in different ways according to social, psychological and contextual factors, besides any understanding of probability.

g) *Scientifically informed citizens are more discriminating in their judgements about science- or technology-related issues.* Additional scientific knowledge can help but is not a guarantee of rational decision-making.

If this is how we use science as adults, then the notion of science for specific purposes may be helpful in determining suitable learning experiences for pupils. We do need to be clear about how learning any particular science topic is going to assist the future citizen and also give consideration to the pupils' role in determining the direction of their own learning.

What Science Content?

We have already seen that the boundaries of science as a collection of disciplines are not clear. Both ASE and the Nuffield Foundation Seminar Series, in considering the future of the science curriculum, have had difficulty in identifying the *essential* concepts of science (ASE, 1998; Millar, 1997; Ratcliffe, 1997). Suggested criteria for determination of which concepts are appropriate for pupils to explore emerged from the ASE consultation, as a modification of those from Project 2061 (AAAS, 1989):

The core content in science should be of:

- *Human and philosophic significance*
  - contributing to learners' understanding of the world;
  - illuminating the way that scientific ideas develop over time;
  - showing the impact of scientific ideas on cultural development.
- *Scientific significance*
  - the content should aim to show how scientists model the world to understand it;
  - ideas should suggest explanations and lead to fruitful development;
  - the range of ideas chosen should include those currently being used by the scientific community and they should also reflect the history of science.
- *Personal significance*
  Relevant content includes:
  - ideas which are immediately accessible;
  - preparation for the future as a citizen in a technological world;
  - development of ideas within appropriate social, personal and industrial contexts.

You might like to use this as a checklist for the science content you currently teach.

Science for Whom?

The discussion so far has centred on science education for future citizens. Should the science education for future scientists be any different? This question relates to when, if at anytime, specialisation should appear in the compulsory curriculum through deliberate choice of development in one area of knowledge at the expense of others.

Future scientists are also future citizens. A different core curriculum for future scientists could neglect essential elements of personal and scientific development (Figs 1.1A and 1.1B). However, providing exactly the same curriculum diet for all up to 16 ignores the differences of individuals.

Science 5–16: A statement of policy (DES, 1985) contains ten principles of science curriculum implementation, which may be useful in considering the implementation of purposes:

a) *breadth* – essentially the three strands of 'scientific literacy'
b) *balance* – across main conceptual areas of science and between knowledge and processes
c) *relevance* – relating to everyday and future experiences
d) *differentiation* – providing essential experience of broad and balanced science yet catering for different standards of achievement
e) *equal opportunities* – particularly relating to gender
f) *continuity* – building on foundations set in earlier phases of education
g) *progression* – developing progressively deeper understanding and competence
h) *links across the curriculum* – links particularly with literacy and numeracy in the primary school; links across the curriculum particularly with mathematics and technology in secondary
i) *teaching methods and approaches* – emphasising practical, investigate and problem-solving activities
j) *assessment* – using methods which recognise skills and processes as well as knowledge and which allow pupils to show what they can do rather than what they cannot do.

These hold true today, yet it remains a challenge to fulfil all of these principles. Squaring principles of breadth and balance with those of equal opportunities and differentiation is not easy. Yet this has to be tackled if the interests and potential of all pupils in science are to be met.

The rest of this book is about realising the purposes of science education.

About the Author

Mary Ratcliffe was Chair of ASE during 1996/7. She is currently a senior lecturer in science education at the University of Southampton.

References and Further reading

AAAS (American Association for the Advancement of Science) (1989) *Science for All Americans* (Project 2061). New York: Oxford University Press.

AAAS (1993) *Benchmarks for Science Literacy*. New York: Oxford University Press.

website for AAAS – project 2061 http://project2061.aaas.org/

National Standards – These have been developed for implementation in the USA and relate to achieving goals of 'scientific literacy' : http://www.nas.edu

ASE (1998) Science Education 2000+ Summary Report *Education in Science* 176 17–20.

DES (1985) *Science 5–16: A statement of policy*. London: HMSO.

DfE (1995) *Science in the National Curriculum*. London: HMSO.

Driver, R., Leach, J., Millar, R., and Scott, P. (1996) *Young people's images of science* Buckingham: Open University Press.

Besides reporting on research into primary and secondary pupils' views of the nature of science, there is a very readable overview of perspectives on the nature of science.

Jenkins, E. (1997a) Towards a functional public understanding of science. In Levinson, R. and Thomas, J. (Eds) *Science Today. Problem or Crisis* London: Routledge.

The whole of this book is worth reading for its range of perspectives on science and science education.

Jenkins, E. (1997b) Scientific and technological literacy for citizenship: what can we learn from research and other evidence. In Sjoberg, S. and Kallerud, E. (Eds) *Science Technology and Citizenship.* Oslo: NIFU.

Layton, D. (1993) *Technology's challenge to science education*. Buckingham: Open University Press.

Millar, R. (1993) Science Education and Public Understanding of Science. In Hull, R. (Ed) *ASE Secondary Science Teachers' Handbook* Hemel Hempstead: Simon and Schuster.

Millar, R (1996) Towards a science curriculum for public understanding. *School Science Review* 77(280) 7–18.

NCC (National Curriculum Council) (1989) *Science. Non-Statutory Guidance.* York: NCC.

Nott, M. and Wellington, J. (1993) Your nature of science profile: an activity for science teachers. *School Science Review* 75 (270) 109–112.

Nuffield Foundation Seminars – *Beyond 2000: Science Education for the future* (London, Kings College):

Ogborn, J. (Ed) (1996) Report of seminar 1 *Science Education: Is there a problem?*

Millar, R. (Ed) (1997) Report of seminar 2 *Criteria for an appropriate science curriculum.*

Ratcliffe, M. (Ed) (1997) Report of seminar 3 *Towards new models of the science curriculum.*

Scottish CCC (1996) *Science Education in Scottish Schools – Looking to the future.* Dundee: Scottish CCC.

1.2 Quality In Science Education

Bob Ponchaud

Good progress made by pupils in their learning is a key characteristic of quality education. This chapter discusses the factors contributing to high-quality learning concentrating on the elements of good teaching, particularly subject knowledge, planning and variety. Striving for further improvement, suggestions are given for future developments.

Quality Science – Effective and Affective

In any occupation professional self-esteem comes in large measure from the belief that one is 'doing a worthwhile job' and 'doing it well'. Few would disagree that teaching science is worthwhile but it is not always quite so easy to be sure that one is 'doing it well' since this involves having clear ideas about what constitutes quality. All teachers know what it is like when things are not going according to plan in the classroom but a feeling for quality is perhaps less instinctive.

A quality artefact is one which closely meets its specification; a quality tool performs well and lasts; the features of artistic quality are more difficult to define! An essential characteristic of quality education is the *progress* made by children. Only if pupils are making real gains can the purposes of education be considered as being fulfilled. For this reason Chapter 1.1 focuses on the purposes of science education and the rationale for science in the school curriculum. Whatever pupils' individual starting points may be, high-quality science education will carry them forward and extend what they know, understand and can do. This is necessary but not sufficient for surely quality science education will also generate interest, motivation and enthusiasm; it will be both *effective* and *affective*.

As Brian Woolnough (1995) argues:

> It [science] should involve the affective as well as the cognitive aspects of a student's life. It is not sufficient only to be concerned with what students know and can do; one must also be concerned with whether they want to do it. It is of fundamental importance to develop students' emotional involvement with their work; to develop their motivation, their commitment, their enjoyment and creativity in science – for without these any knowledge and skills they acquire in the subject will be of no avail.

Quality in science education, as in everything else, has many dimensions. For all teachers the classroom experience of pupils is itself paramount and will receive their first consideration. All teachers will also wish to contribute to those aspects of the work of a school or department which influence the quality of what takes place in the classroom. The curriculum, its planning and assessment will clearly have a direct effect on what an individual teacher does. Less obvious but equally important are the ways in which pupils' social, moral, spiritual and cultural development is supported; the guidance they are given and how learning relates to the world outside school. Quality in science education cannot just be about science. (See Chapter 2.5.)

The ultimate goal of teachers in any subject must be to produce high-quality teaching all the time! Whilst that remains the ambition it is as well to appreciate that, as Hilary Wilce put it: ... *whatever recipe is chosen, it's all in the end, in the detail. Good teaching is painstaking, tedious stuff...* (TES). As she goes on to remind the reader, quality is about doing the routine things consistently and in a way which takes account of pupils' needs as well as on occasions teaching that truly inspirational lesson.

High Quality Learning – What Should Pupils Gain?

What are the science specific features of quality in education? It is useful to decide firstly what pupils should gain from their school experience of science. As a result of their activities in science lessons pupils should be developing the following:

- knowledge and understanding of science which they can apply
- the skills of scientific enquiry
- some appreciation of the nature and limitations of science
- an awareness of how the applications of science affect their lives and others'
- interest in and curiosity about science
- an ability to work safely and show respect for living things and the environment.

This is not a unique representation of the goals of science by any means. It does however represent the breadth of the subject and has implications for the range of techniques, activities and contexts which will need to be utilised if quality is to be achieved. It is, for example, difficult to see how progress can be made in the areas listed without a blend of practical activity, discussion, book-related learning, use of IT and investigation featuring in lessons.

Whilst it is relatively easy to argue that the attributes listed above should be developed in all pupils as part of their science education the discussion continues about their nature and the emphasis which each should be given. Most would agree that a rounded science education should include the development of the 'skills of scientific enquiry' but reaching agreement concerning what these skills are and how they can be developed is not such an easy matter! Teachers, as well as politicians and academics, have a part to play in this legitimate debate for ultimately it is they who will have to translate the resulting curriculum into workable classroom practice. In this chapter it is assumed that the first responsibility of teachers of science is to work towards high-quality delivery of the statutory curriculum whilst taking an active part in discussion of the curriculum organised by the ASE and others.

It is important that pupils also develop within science the ability to:

- communicate scientific findings using appropriate literacy skills
- display, manipulate and analyse scientific data using appropriate mathematical skills

- use ICT to capture, store, retrieve, analyse and present information.

These abilities are important to the development of pupils' scientific literacy and also contribute to the broader curriculum. Quality science education will therefore both utilise and extend these capabilities and make demands on pupils which are consistent with expectations elsewhere in the curriculum.

The Importance of Teaching – Making a Difference

There is little doubt that teaching is the most significant of the factors which contribute to high standards in science education. Analysis of inspection data suggests that the quality of teaching has a four times greater influence on achievement than any of the other 'contributory factors' which are judged in the OFSTED Framework for Inspection. There is certainly substance behind the slogan 'teachers make a difference'!

The criteria for evaluating the quality of teaching which are incorporated into the OFSTED Handbook for Inspection represent a distillation of the experience of HM Inspectors over many years. The criteria are useful pointers for all those seeking an answer to the question, 'What are the features of effective teaching?' Judgements are based on the extent to which teachers:

- have a secure knowledge and understanding of the subjects or areas they teach
- set high expectations so as to challenge pupils and deepen their knowledge and understanding
- plan effectively
- employ methods and organisational strategies which match curricular objectives and the needs of all pupils
- manage pupils well and achieve high standards of discipline
- use time and resources effectively
- assess pupils' work thoroughly and constructively, and use assessments to inform teaching
- use homework effectively to reinforce and/or extend what is learned in school.

These are of course generic criteria which have to be translated in a science context; this is done in much of the rest of this book. There are however important issues of quality particularly in relation to the first two criteria.

Subject Knowledge

As recently as 1994 HMI reported that, Shortcomings in (primary) teachers' own scientific understanding remain a serious obstacle to achieving higher standards (Subjects and Standards, 1994–5, OFSTED). It would be wrong to suggest that primary-class teachers have since become science specialists but great strides forward have been made. Teachers have gained familiarity with the National Curriculum requirements and schools have worked hard to make the best use of available expertise in science by strategies such as class swapping and short-term specialist teaching as well as using INSET time to share ideas. The quality of whole-school planning has improved and this has provided valuable support to those teachers with little background in science. Nevertheless there is still much that can be done to further improve subject knowledge and expertise; there is a role here for both primary and secondary specialists. Primary science co-ordinators can do much to pass on their expertise to others by means of support materials, topic workshops and wherever possible working with colleagues. Secondary teachers can contribute their expertise whilst at the same time learning from primary practice and so improving the key-stage transition.

High Expectations and Key Stage Transfer

In order to have appropriately high expectations of pupils it is necessary to know what they have already achieved. Across each key stage boundary there is a danger that continuity will be lost and expectations will be too low. This is particularly true of the transfer from Key Stage 2 to Key Stage 3. Primary science has made massive strides forward so the base on which teachers are building in early secondary school has changed. The appropriate starting points for pupils on transfer to secondary school will depend on individual attainment but also, to some extent, on the way in which science is organised and taught in Key Stage 2. All too often the achievements of pupils are not fully recognised or built upon early in their secondary experience because scientific ideas are encountered in very different contexts to those used in primary school or the language used to describe them is unfamiliar. Curriculum liaison between primary and secondary schools has improved considerably but remains one of the main issues of quality for Key Stage 3 science.

The Importance of Planning – Small Steps towards Big Ideas

The foundations for good science teaching and learning are laid outside the classroom or laboratory. Successful learning is much more likely when teachers have a clear view of what they want children to learn from an activity (objectives), the processes which will carry them towards these goals and what pupils will be able to do as a result (outcomes). It is also becoming increasingly clear from research that it is important to be aware of what ideas pupils have to start with, including sometimes some stubborn misconceptions! (See Chapters 2.1, 3.2 and 3.5.)

It is also important when planning to take account of notions of continuity and progression (see Chapter 3.6). This is well expressed by Driver *et al* (1994):

> *Teaching science with children's thinking in mind depends upon careful planning in which continuity of curriculum is designed for progression in pupils' ideas.*

> *The term 'progression' is applied to something that happens inside a learner's head: thinking about experience and ideas, children develop their ideas. Some aspects of their learning may happen quite quickly and easily, whereas others happen in very small steps over a number of years.*

> *Continuity on the other hand is something organised by the teacher: it*

describes the relationship between experiences, activities and ideas which pupils meet over a period of time, in a curriculum which is structured to support learning. Curriculum continuity cannot guarantee progression. Its role is to structure ideas and experiences for learners in a way which will help them to move their conceptual understanding forward in scientific terms.

Our knowledge about the ways in which children's ideas about science develop changes through experience and formal research (see, for example, Chapters 2.1 and 2.2). Fortunately, for the teacher in the classroom, much of what experience suggests supports good progression is now enshrined in published schemes and syllabuses. For practical purposes planning will be based largely on established thinking but an awareness of changing ideas is part of professional development, an attribute of the 'reflective practitioner'.

Great benefit can be gained from joint planning of work since experiences of success can be shared, ideas about effective approaches pooled and specialist knowledge utilised. In both primary and secondary science it is common for work to be divided into topics or modules and, especially during times of rapid curriculum change, these have often been planned by individuals in order to make the task manageable. Inevitably there are times when 'the joins show' and the pupils' experience of science is fragmented or involves repetition. There are fertile links between different areas of science which need to be exploited to help pupils gain a coherent understanding of the key ideas. Joint, or at least shared, planning is a means of promoting these connections and enabling teachers to share professional experience and expertise.

Effective planning in science has the following features:

- Work is structured so as to build progressively on pupils' previous knowledge and understanding.
- Opportunities are included for pupils to think about and discuss their emerging scientific ideas.
- Experimental and investigative work is incorporated in such a way that it links with and builds upon pupils' scientific knowledge and understanding.
- Connections between related areas of science are made explicit (see, for example, Chapters 2.6, 2.7, 2.8 and 3.1).

Variety – the Spice?

One of the distinguishing features of science education is the emphasis rightly given to practical activity. For many pupils the most memorable experience of their first year of secondary education is lighting a Bunsen burner for the first time! Some, alas, also gain the impression that 'real science' has to take place in a laboratory. Primary science teaching has wider horizons! The interest which most pupils show in practical work is clearly something to be exploited and the good use of experimental work will remain the principal strategy in the effective science teacher's repertoire. Nevertheless there are many other effective and motivating activities and approaches to learning science which the science teacher can draw upon.

Many of the schools and departments that have carried out an 'audit' of their approaches to science teaching have been surprised by the outcomes. It is a common experience to find that the range of activities is large but the incidence of some types is both lower and more variable than anticipated. For example, although IT may feature in schemes of work for science the actual use of this may vary between teachers often depending on their confidence in handling work with computers and perceptions of its value. Most teachers have a 'preferred style' and it is understandable that this predominates especially when they are under the pressures of rapid curriculum change or inspection! Quality science education will however incorporate a range of teaching activities and approaches with the common aim of engaging pupils (see Chapters 3.7 and 3.8).

A useful strategy adopted by some schools with the aim of increasing variety in science is to link an audit of existing practice with the setting of targets for future practice and agreement to try new approaches. Typically this might involve the following:

- making sure that experimental work has clear and specific learning objectives communicated to pupils
- selecting illustrative class practical, investigation or participative demonstration according to the intended purpose
- the use of activities which develop the skills of investigation as well as the carrying out of 'whole investigations'
- giving opportunities for pupils to express and discuss their ideas as well as responding to tightly-framed questions
- providing opportunities for some extended reading about science beyond the double-page spread and, especially in the primary phase, reading fiction as well as non-fiction with a science dimension
- setting science in a social or technological context in which pupils are confronted with issues as well as concepts
- the use of IT (as facilities permit) for research, data logging, display and processing.

This list can, of course, be extended in ways which depend on the interests of teachers and the resources available. The essential elements are clarity of and fitness for purpose and the confidence of teachers in the approach being used. There is evidence that, just as teachers have preferred styles, pupils learn and are motivated in different ways so perhaps 'variety is the spice'.

Science with a Social Life!

When secondary pupils are asked about their reasons for not choosing to study science beyond what is compulsory they often mention the relative lack of discussion and relevance; science is seen to be individual. As one student put it, "Science doesn't have a social life!". There are also strong indications that science thrives where extra-curricular activities are strong and varied. Certainly schools that have broadened their scientific horizons beyond the laboratory report the benefits of doing so. There are also benefits to be gained from involving local employers and those in science-related professions in school-based activities (see Chapter 2.8).

The first responsibility of any teacher must, of course, be to deliver the statutory curriculum in an effective way; but few would wish to stop there. The list of activities which can be used to enrich science is almost endless but includes:

- CREST and other award schemes
- visits to the growing number of 'hands on' science centres
- partnerships with neighbourhood scientists
- science fairs on site
- science 'public understanding' days in the community
- off-timetable enrichment days
- science magazines produced by pupils using school IT facilities
- using secondary pupils to organise science activities for primary pupils.

Recognising and Improving Quality

Teaching is, by its nature and organisation, an occupation in which it is difficult to know how what one is doing compares with what is going on elsewhere. Opportunities to observe colleagues in the same school are few and time to find out about the issues and opportunities for schools other than one's own are equally scarce. How then can the reflective teacher arrive at a professional decision about the quality of their own practice in order to move forward?

The two principal mechanisms by which teachers can gauge their own professional progress and that of their school or department are self-review and external inspection. External inspection carried out by Registered Inspectors working under contract to OFSTED provides a basis for the national evaluation of schools as well as identifying the strengths and weaknesses of individual schools so that they may improve the quality of education provided. In relation to science, inspections will involve evaluation of:

- pupils' attainment in relation to national expectations or standards, drawing on evidence of what pupils know, understand and can do by the end of each key stage
- progress made in relation to pupils' prior attainment
- pupils' attitudes to learning
- any strengths and weaknesses in teaching and other factors which contribute to standards (see Chapter 4.4).

The experience of inspection is inevitably stressful but can also provide valuable information and professional development. As well as generating reports on individual schools inspection data is used by OFSTED to provide a national overview of subject work and aspects of school life. These are published in various forms including regular booklets about science. These enable teachers to set their own work in a broad context and find out about national issues of quality.

Self review will normally involve both monitoring of what is being done and evaluation of its effectiveness. Targets for future progress will also be set, often incorporated into a departmental development plan. Local Authorities often have their own frameworks for school self-review and for science the ASE has published both primary and secondary self-evaluation documents (NAIGS/ASE, 1996, 1997). These take the main headings of the OFSTED framework and translate the criteria into subject specific terms to aid on-going evaluation. These or other self-review publications can be used to help schools or departments through the five stage cycle of self-improvement:

- How well are we doing?
- How do we compare with other similar schools?
- What more should we aim to achieve – this year?
- What must we do to make it happen?
- How can we review progress?

Is Good 'Good Enough'?

Any discussion about quality is bound to set out high ideals and therefore runs the risk of disheartening those who seek to meet them! It is difficult to balance encouragement and challenge but fortunately where science education is concerned there is much to celebrate; much that will spur all those involved to want even better. The following quotations show both what has been achieved and areas of attention to make what is good even better!

Primary

> *Standards in science have improved and the performance of English pupils in science now compares favourably with that of pupils in other countries. Four-fifths of pupils achieve or exceed the expected National Curriculum level in science at Key Stage 1 and more than two thirds at Key Stage 2. In a recent international survey Year 5 pupils in England obtained mean science scores which were exceeded by pupils in only three of the other 25 countries which took part.*
>
> *Science in primary schools has made much progress over recent years; standards have been raised and pupils now enter secondary schooling with a better foundation of knowledge, skills and terminology than previously. Inspection shows that this favourable trend is continuing but that there are some persistent variations in standards within and between schools that need to be addressed if primary science is to gain further ground and all children make steady progress. Attention needs to be paid to:*
>
> – *the relative weakness of Years 3 and 4;*
> – *making the best use of available specialist expertise;*
> – *raising expectations by monitoring pupils' progress in science;*
> – *ensuring high standards across the whole Programme of Study;*
> – *making sure that literacy and numeracy are supported by and developed in science.* (OFSTED, 1998a)

Secondary

> *From 1993 there has been steady improvement in standards in science. In particular the sharper focus for lessons, clearer objectives identified by teach-*

ers, and better use of class time has contributed to an improvement in pupils' knowledge base. The proportion of pupils reaching the expected level in science national tests has risen slowly to six out of ten, a similar proportion to other core subjects. International comparisons confirm this broadly positive picture with standards comparing favourably with those in other Western European countries. Results in double award science GCSE have shown steady improvement and at A-level, whilst overall numbers of entries for science subjects have declined, students taking science subjects achieve well and obtain good grades in relation to their GCSE performance. A-level results in modular science courses have also been good, despite the fact that lack of success in early modules has raised questions about the preparedness of some students for these elements of the syllabus.

This is a particularly encouraging picture given that the science curriculum has been subject to a number of changes.

There remain some issues for schools to address if science is to continue to flourish and maintain its international standing:

– Pupils understanding of underlying scientific concepts remains insecure, and they are insufficiently able to apply their knowledge to new contexts.
– Standards in experimental and investigatory work have consistently remained below those in other attainment targets.
– More needs to be done to raise the status and popularity of science with pupils at all levels. (OFSTED, 1998b)

About the Author

Bob Ponchaud was an HM Inspector based in London before the establishment of OFSTED. He is now the Subject Adviser for Science and the point of reference for all matters relating to science within OFSTED. Before becoming an HMI he occupied a variety of posts including Head of Science in two large comprehensives. His other experience includes school-based research, writing textbooks and examining science.

References and Further Reading

NAIGS/ASE (1996) *School Science Department Self-Evaluation Document*, Hatfield, ASE.

NAIGS/ASE (1997) *Primary Science Self-Review Document*, Hatfield, ASE.

N.B. These useful publications use OFSTED framework headings but the criteria included reflect interpretations made by the writers (National Advisers and Inspectors Group in Science/ASE) and should not be seen as adding to those in the OFSTED handbook.

Driver, R., Squires, A., Rushworth, P. and Wood-Robinson, V. (1994) *Making sense of secondary science,* London, Routledge.

OFSTED (1998a) *Standards in Primary Science,* London, The Stationery Office.
OFSTED (1998b) *Secondary Review 1993–7,* London, The Stationery Office.
Woolnough, B.E. (1995). *Effective Science Teaching*, Milton Keynes: Open University Press.

1.3 The Last Ten Years; the Next Ten Years

Wynne Harlen

This chapter has three rather that the two main sections which the title might suggest. It begins with a look back at some significant changes which have taken place from the 1980s through the 1990s. The introduction of the National Curriculum in England and Wales, and its counterparts in other countries of the UK, plays a large part in these changes, particularly in terms of the status of the subject, with several knock-on effects. Other trends discussed in the first section relate to: the understanding of what science at the primary level means – its identity; the increased interest from research; the sharp change in attention to assessment and record-keeping; the shift in the basis for national monitoring; the debate about process and content learning outcomes; the nature of learning in primary science; and finally the seriousness with which international comparisons are viewed in the late 1990s compared with ten years ago.

The second section deals with current concerns which are drawn from discussion of trends in the first section: the balance between process and content; the teacher's role; the background knowledge of science of teachers; and the lack of effective formative assessment.

The third section tries to look ahead. Some aspects of change in the next ten years can be fairly confidently stated, for example, the increased role on information and communications technology, but others are more speculative. These relate to an increased emphasis on key skills and the development of broad over-arching concepts, the treatment of science and technology in the curriculum and the role of pupils in helping teachers to manage their learning.

Introduction

Although 10 years is a short timespan in terms of historical time, in terms of the development of primary science, the last decade encompasses an enormous change of historic dimensions. This reflective chapter begins with a look at this brief but crowded history which helps us to put into context some topics of current concern. In turn, reflecting on the aspects of teaching and learning in primary science which are seen at the present time as problematic, provides the basis for considering the future. Looking ahead should need no justification at a time when forward planning and target setting are the hall marks of managing education! Although risky in this fast changing world, it is useful to consider what might be in order to reflect on the desirability of certain prospects and what might be done to facilitate the positive trends and avoid the negative ones.

The Last Ten Years

The last ten years takes us back to the period just before the implementation of the National Curriculum in England and Wales, the Northern Ireland Curriculum, and the 5–14 National Guidelines in Scotland. The changes since that time can be characterised in terms of some general trends. The notion of trends avoids the suggestion of abrupt change or of uniformity in practice at any stage either now or in the past.

Status

At the beginning of the 1980s the generally unsatisfactory state of primary science had been well exposed by the 1978 HMI report into primary education. This was followed by several important statements by HMI (DES, 1983) and the DES (1985) advising that science should be a part of every child's education from the age of 5 to 16. There was also increased attention to science at the primary level prompted by the reports of the Assessment of Performance Unit (APU) surveys. Action was taken in the form of the Educational Support Grant scheme which provided funds for training of advisory teachers in science and in a few other subjects. Despite these initiatives, however, science teaching remained patchy. Although the incidence of good practice was increasing, the change was not fast enough for the government. Science was swept up in the reform that culminated in the National Curriculum in England and Wales and, as part of the 'core', was not only subject to specification of what was to be taught and learned, but was to be included in national testing at ages 7, 11 and 14.

The change from an 'occasional' part of the curriculum to designation as a core subject required massive support in terms of staff development and resources. Extended courses were made available, particularly for science co-ordinators and these seemed to have a considerable effect. Research carried out at the University of Exeter showed a dramatic improvement in teachers' perceived competence in teaching science from 1989 to 1991. In this study, over 900 teachers in England were asked about how competent they felt to teach various subjects of the National Curriculum, just after it was introduced in 1989. Science was rated low; eighth out of ten subjects. But two years later it had risen to third place, just behind English and mathematics. The researchers ascribed the change to the allocation of resources, both human and material, to science teaching in the intervening years, together with the comprehensive map of the subject that the Orders provided (Bennett, Wragg, Carre and Carter, 1992).

In Scotland, where the national guidelines are non-statutory, the guidelines for Environmental Studies, of which science forms a component, were published in 1993. A survey at that time showed the confidence of primary teachers to be low; very similar to the 1989 findings in England. A repeat survey showed only a very small improvement in confidence by 1996 and the rate of implementation of the guidelines was slow. Thus is seemed that although publication of guidelines and target outcomes was important, this alone is not enough (Harlen, 1997).

Identity

The National Curriculum Orders and the 5–14 National Guidelines defined for the first time what should be learned and what should be taught in science at the primary level. This specification separated science from other subjects with which it frequently had been closely connected. In particular it was distinguished from mathematics and from technology. Although the separation on paper does not require separation in teaching, it became incumbent on teachers to know when they were teaching science and when children were learning it. This is far easier, particularly for those new to it, if science is taught as a separate subject and an almost inevitable trend has been to see science lessons rather than science components within broad topics.

So there has been a rapid move from the position a decade ago when many teachers were uncertain about what science was (process? content? problem solving?) and about how far to go in pursuing a topic, to one where what children should learn at various stages has been set out. Issues remain about the emphasis on various aspects as we will see later in discussing current debates.

Research

A symptom of the raised status of science at the primary level is the increased attention that it has received from researchers. The 1980s saw a good deal of research activity. Some of this was sparked by the APU findings which not only gave evidence of children's ideas and process skills but provided the instruments for investigating these in different contexts. The APU findings were directly used in the research at the secondary level conducted by the Children's Learning in Science (CLIS) project. At the primary level, two extended projects were begun which were to lead to important developments. The SPACE (Science Processes and Concepts Exploration) project sponsored by the Nuffield Foundation was investigating children's scientific ideas (SPACE, 1990–98), and the STAR (Science Teaching Action Research) project, funded by the Leverhulme Trust, was concerned with classroom practice in relation to process skills.

When the National Curriculum was published the SPACE project extended its research work, which was carried out in collaboration with teachers, to cover all the concepts in the areas of knowledge and understanding. The research findings were then used to create the teachers' guides and other materials of the Nuffield Primary Science Project (1995). The SPACE work was largely responsible for bringing 'constructivism' into common discourse about primary science teaching, although, like many ideas in education, it had roots in earlier work, particularly that of Piaget.

The speed with which interest in children's own understandings of science took hold, in in-service and pre-service teacher education courses and in teachers' classroom research is a remarkable feature of the past decade. Rather than assuming that the children would not have any ideas about a topic unless it had been 'taught', teachers and researchers began to investigate children's own ideas. Hardly an issue of ASE's *Primary Science Review* during this time was without an article describing some aspect of children's thinking that these investigations revealed.

The impact of the STAR project has been less obvious than in the case of SPACE, perhaps because it was spread in at least two different directions. On one hand it added to understanding of the role of process skills in learning science and to understanding of how to help children in developing their investigative skills. On the other hand it developed ways of assessing process skills which remain highly relevant to formative assessment today (Schilling *et al*, 1990).

A further significant area for research has been the investigation of teachers' own understanding of concepts and skills and of their confidence in teaching science. Concern about primary teachers' poor background in science was firmly articulated HM Inspectors in 1978: 'the most severe obstacle to the improvement of science the primary school is that many existing teachers lack a working knowledge of elementary science appropriate to children of this age'. However, it was the explicit listing, in the various curriculum statements or guidelines, of what understanding teachers were expected to develop in their pupils that brought into sharp focus the concern about whether teachers had the necessary understanding themselves. Previously it had been possible for teachers to concentrate on areas – often biological – where they felt more confident and to avoid the ones – mainly in physical science – where they felt less secure. In the past decade this was no longer possible. Through the work of the Oxford-based Primary *Science Teachers Project* and the Edinburgh-based project *on Primary Teachers' Understanding of Concepts in Science and Technology* (Harlen *et al*, 1995) much is now known about the scientific understanding of primary teachers and its impact on practice. It is recognised further that we need to understand the role of subject knowledge in primary teaching. This is a focus for current attention, related to the continuing debate about emphasis on skills and knowledge at the primary level.

Assessment and Record Keeping

In the early 1980s a survey of record keeping showed that there was hardly any assessment and record keeping of learning in science (Clift, Weiner and Wilson, 1981). The situation improved during the '80s, influenced by the APU examples of how aspects of learning other than factual knowledge could be assessed. But the greatest change and challenge came, of course, with the implementation of the National Curriculum and the requirement for teachers to assess levels of achievement. Although science is included in national testing only in England and Wales, in all four countries of the UK teachers are expected to record achievement in science and include it in their reports to parents. Ideally they should also be using assessment formatively, in helping teaching decisions. Unfortunately, the demands of summative assessment have dominated assessment activity and the distinction between assessment for different purposes appears to have been lost. (See also Chapter 3.2).

National Monitoring

The national monitoring conducted in England, Wales and Northern Ireland by the APU from 1980 to 1984 was terminated on the introduction of the national tests for pupils of ages 7 and 11 in the primary school and 14 in the secondary school. The APU's extensive bank of test items, both practical and written, had been used to report performance across a very wide range of skills and areas of understanding in science. Its sophisticated sampling procedures enabled this information to be collected for the whole age group whilst each pupil involved only had to be tested for less than an hour. In the national tests, by contrast, all pupils take the same items and the information is confined to the amount of testing that any one pupil can reasonably be given and thus is a very limited measure of science performance. Moreover, the national tests in England and Wales at age 11 are restricted to knowledge and understanding. Since the test results are used to compare schools' performances with each other in league tables, there is a tendency for teachers to give more attention to what is to be tested and so rather less to practical work and investigative skills. (See also Chapter 3.3)

Learning Outcomes

The debate about the relative importance of process skills and content knowledge in primary science is one of very long standing. The process emphasis was more in keeping with the climate of thinking about primary schools in the 60s and early 70s but after that there was a growing opinion that content has to be considered and a recognition of the interdependence of the development of skills and concepts.

Unfortunately a way has not yet been found to set down in a curriculum both skill and conceptual outcomes in a way which preserves and signals their interdependence. The continued separation of skills from knowledge and understanding in official documents has done little to encourage a balanced view of learning outcomes. Further, as already mentioned, the preference given to assessing knowledge in the national tests has tended to push practice towards emphasising content. However, as we will discuss later, there are new influences which may well set the pendulum swinging back in favour of skills as important outcomes of learning.

View of Learning

Since the 1980s we have moved away from the uncritical embracing of various versions of discovery learning. These had arisen as part of the movement to emphasise children 'learning by doing' as a reaction to previous formal teaching. However, discovery and its adaptations, such as guided discovery, ignore all the evidence now accumulated that children have ideas already formed and bring these to new investigations. What they do, and what sense they make of what they find, is influenced by these initial ideas, so their learning is not a *discovery* of new ideas but a *development* of ideas which they bring and are constructing for themselves. Various types of constructivist learning exist but what they have in common is taking children's existing ideas as the starting point. Where there are differences it is in the way in which the information is then used. (See also Chapter 2.1)

International Ranking

There are two trends over recent years in relation to international ranking of pupils' performance. One is in the performance of pupils in comparison with those in other countries and the other is in the attention paid to such comparisons. To take the latter first, there is a notable difference in the attention given to the Third

International Mathematics and Science Survey (TIMSS) compared with its predecessors. By 1997 it was no longer acceptable, as it was a decade before, to ignore the findings of such surveys on the ground that what they tested did not coincide with what was valued in our science teaching.

In terms of the results, the TIMSS results showed pupils in science had improved relative to other countries. England was ranked 7th out of 24 countries for the performance of 9 year olds in year 4, whilst Scotland's position was little changed, being ranked 12th.

Current Concerns

A number of points of concern or controversy have run across this discussion of trends in the past ten years. These are matters of on-going debate and deserve some further comments in the context of 'where we are now'. The main ones are the matter of the process/content balance, the teacher's role in constructivist learning, teachers' subject knowledge, and the need for greater understanding and application of formative assessment. But the agenda of current concerns is also set by the vision of the future. We can anticipate considerable changes in teaching and learning in all subjects in the next ten years and it is essential that we begin to consider how to prepare for them. Foremost among the foreseeable changes is the impact of Information and Communications Technology (ICT).

The Process/Content Balance

The debate about the process/content balance continues to run on because it embraces wider debates about the nature of scientific knowledge, about learning and about values. We may agree that the aim of science education is understanding of the world around but disagree about how this understanding is to be reached. If learning with understanding is valued, then there is emphasis on children starting from their own ideas and using evidence from their investigations to change and develop these ideas so that they gradually become more widely applicable and so 'bigger'. But the sense that children make of evidence will only lead to greater *scientific* understanding if the processes of enquiry and of thinking are carried out scientifically. That means, for example, that evidence has to be gathered systematically, making fair comparisons and valid measurements, and that all the evidence is considered in forming conclusions; in other words, that the process skills are used.

However, science process skills cannot be used and developed unless children are working on appropriate content, that is, content that is relevant, amenable to scientific investigation and within their grasp to understand at a meaningful level. Conversely, using and developing process skills – thinking skills as well as 'doing' skills – enables children to learn with understanding. True conceptual development cannot take place if children are not engaged in doing their own thinking.

Thus both content and process skills require careful attention in teaching. A neglect of process skills means that children have to take ideas as given by the teacher or the textbook and there is a great deal of experience that shows this is unlikely to lead to understanding. There is no doubt that the National Curriculum has produced a tension for teachers between the often slow process of working from children's ideas and the need to 'cover' the content prescribed – a tension not present a decade ago. A neglect of content, on the other hand, means that some ideas relating to understanding the world around are not developed and there is a poor basis for progression and continuity in learning science from 5 to 16. This optimum balance has yet to be struck. It depends not only on the curriculum and on teachers' planning but on the role the teacher plays in the classroom, to which we now turn.

The Teacher's Role in Constructivist Teaching

The best known and agreed feature of constructivist teaching is that it starts from children's ideas. Various ways of finding out what these ideas are have been developed, as for example, by the Nuffield Primary Science team, who suggest use of. talking and open questioning; annotated drawings; sorting and classifying; writing down ideas; log books and diaries (Teachers' Guides, 1995). Finding out the ideas is the easy and fascinating part, but what is the next step? If the ideas are unscientific how are they to be replaced by the scientific view? If they are consistent with the scientific view but limited, how do teachers take them further and how far should they go? These are important questions to which convincing answers are still being sought.

Some suggestions for dealing with unscientific ideas depend on providing evidence which conflicts with the children's ideas and so challenges them to reconsider their ideas. In this approach there is a risk of making the child feel that he or she is wrong and this can be de-motivating for future learning. An alternative is to explore the children's reasons for holding an idea, and to find out if the idea arises from an interpretation of evidence or from hearsay. Another approach is to discuss the words the child is using and find out the meaning that is being attached to them, for there is often miscommunication because of the child's limited vocabulary or use of inappropriate analogies. (See also Chapter 2.1).

These steps will help the teacher to understand the child's ideas but they do not avoid the dilemma of whether to give children the 'right' answer, supposing that this is known. No general formula can be given for solving this problem, for the appropriate response in any particular case must depend on the child, the context and the concept involved. However what is important is to give the children access to different ideas which can come from other children, from further investigations, from secondary sources, or from the teacher. These ideas should be considered by the children as *possible* answers, not the answer. This step of gathering possibilities, by arranging discussion and making information sources accessible is as important to the teacher's role as providing opportunities for practical investigations. Equally important is the role of the teacher in questioning and encouraging the development of process skills (thinking as well as doing) and fostering a commitment in children to seek and use evidence which is essential to constructing ideas consistent with the scientific view. (See also Chapter 3.7)

Teachers' Subject Knowledge

The role of the teacher just discussed can be implemented effectively only if teachers have sufficient scientific understanding themselves to know when children's ideas are scientific or unscientific. Given that it is not feasible for primary teachers to have at least an 'A' level, or equivalent, in science, it is important to consider the role of subject knowledge in science teaching. This role is surely not so that teachers can answer all the questions children ask or can transmit knowledge to children. Instead it is so that teachers can help children to their own understanding, so that they can ask questions that lead children to reveal and reflect on their ideas, can avoid 'blind alleys', can provide relevant sources of information and other resources, can identify progress and the next steps that will take it further. These things cannot be done if teachers don't understand the ideas they are aiming for. However they require understanding of broad principles and key ideas rather than a detailed knowledge of facts.

Formative Assessment

The terms used to describe the purposes of assessment as formative or summative have become familiar during the past decade, whereas in the 1980s they would have been considered as unnecessary jargon. The purpose of formative assessment, the process of finding out where children are in their learning and using this to make decisions about the next steps, is helping children rather than grading them. It is not difficult to see that this type of assessment is essential to constructivist approaches to teaching and indeed to any teaching approaches that attempt to match experiences to children's development. Gathering information frequently about children's learning has to be an integral part of such teaching. The theoretical arguments for this find massive support in research which shows unequivocally that the best way to raise standards in education is to improve formative assessment (Black and Wiliam, 1998).

The original idea of assessment in the National Curriculum was that it should have a formative purpose. Unfortunately, it was assumed that results of assessment that serves a formative purpose can also be used for other purposes, that is, to provide summative judgements and, when combined into class and whole school results, for evaluative purposes (DES, 1987). Experience has shown that once the assignment of levels becomes the main focus of attention for assessment, which it has to be if results are to be combined for summative purposes, then the formative function is forgotten. A great deal of effort and resources have been put into increasing the comparability of teachers' judgements of the level of individual pieces of work but little into using the information formatively.

It is worth noting that in Scotland, where science is not tested, and in any case national tests results are not centrally collected and used to create league tables, there is more attention both in official documents and in teachers' resources to formative assessment. It remains a concern in all countries of the UK, however, to provide help for teachers to assess science development as part of their work and to use assessment to improve learning rather than just to monitor it.

The Next Ten Years

Some changes in ways of teaching and understanding seem to swing to and fro like a pendulum, but they do not return to quite the same position; so many other things change in the meantime. Thus it may seem that 'we have been here before' in the case of some of the points made in this section, but this is not so when we look in more depth.

Science and Technology

The separation of science and technology at the primary level has been helpful, in theory, in shaping thinking about the contribution to education of each of these subjects; science aiming at understanding, technology aiming at the development of skills to solve problems in real life contexts. But there is so close a relationship between science and technology in practice, that pursuing one without the other is artificial (and indeed time wasting). In the case of technology, there remains some confusion about what the subject is and this has led to children spending time on constructing artefacts but learning little about technology in the process. More purposeful technological activities could be pursued, for example, if they were related to solving problems encountered in the course of a scientific investigation. Science and technology would be taught in combination – not as science, with technology losing its identity, but as 'science and technology'. A move in this direction will not be a return to making no distinction between the subjects but a recognition of the contribution of both to children's development of ideas and skills. (See also Chapter 2.7.)

Key Skills across the Curriculum

Following on from the last point, the future may well see a re-emphasis on scientific skills. Again it would be a mistake to see this as a return to 1960s thinking; instead it is a recognition of the importance of the skills that today's learners will need in tomorrow's world. It is widely recognised that we need to create a culture of lifelong learning, since no longer will learning in early life prepare anyone for a life-time of effective activity. So learning how to learn is an essential aim of formal education. Science has a key role to play in its potential to develop communication, critical thinking skills and the ability to find, use and evaluate evidence. Thus the development of skills is likely to regain prominence as part of a curriculum-wide aim of achieving broad and applicable skills.

'Big' rather than 'Small' Ideas

A further related point is that what will be important in an educated person of the future is not detailed knowledge, since there will be an abundance of information of this kind at everyone's finger tips through the expansion of ICT. Rather, the important knowledge will be the possession of 'big' ideas, ones that link a number of small ideas together. It will be essential for teachers to have these over-arching ideas and to be able to relate them to the specific investigations carried out in the classroom. New technology will also be used to help in teacher education and support for developing these ideas.

Information and Communications Technology

In addition to ways already mentioned in which ICT can have a role in science education, it has a direct role in helping children to collect and interpret evidence. It is already possible for children to extend their experience to things which were previously imperceptible to them. For example, they can investigate light intensities using light-sensitive probes, or test out ideas about temperature differences in situations where thermometers cannot be used. Extension of this role of technology will enable children to test their ideas more quickly and more reliably. Young children will be able to collect data and use computers to process it quickly, which will surely advance their development. There is already evidence that the pace of young children's learning increases when they use ICT. What will be needed in order to take advantage of this is careful thinking and research to identify the 'big' ideas and the routes of progress towards them. A priority for the next ten years is the development of a curriculum in which these routes and the progression in key skills are spelled out. (See also Chapter 3.8.)

Teachers' and Pupils' Roles in Learning

With so many other sources of information, the teacher's role will be to manage learning rather than to provide information. Far from implying a return to a vague 'facilitator' role sometimes advocated in the past, this means taking an active part in monitoring learning, sharing this information with children, deciding the next steps and providing the environment in which these steps can be taken. This will include asking probing questions which make children think, setting up situations in which ideas are shared among children and in which new ideas can be given. Sometimes this can best be done in a whole class discussion, but again this is far from a return to traditional teaching. What is also likely to change is the balance between talking and thinking on the one hand and physical activity on the other. The latter will be more purposeful, more focused and often more quickly completed than is common today, given the use of new technologies, leaving more time for thinking and reflecting.

Involving children in taking decisions about their own learning is an important direction of change. Already there are examples of good practice, where teachers take time to talk through work with children, help them to criticise their work constructively and involve them in deciding what they need to improve. The difficulty of finding time to do this is more than compensated by the advantages of children sharing responsibility for their learning. Moreover, the use of technology and the more effective use of practical work should reduce the pressure on time, allowing teachers to re-order their priorities and spend more time on developing the skills and broad areas of understanding that their children need for life in the twenty-first century.

About the Author

Wynne Harlen, OBE, has been Director of the Scottish Council for Research in Education since 1990 and was formerly Professor of Science Education at the University of Liverpool. She has written several books and reports on primary science and has a particular interest in the role of assessment in teaching and learning.

References

Bennett, S. N., Wragg, E. C., Carré, C. G. and Carter, D. S. G. (1992) A longitudinal study of primary teachers' perceived competence in, and concerns about, National Curriculum implementation. *Research Papers in Education* Vol 7, No 1, pp 53–78.

Black, P. J and Wiliam, D (1998) Assessment and classroom learning. *Assessment in Education* 5 (1) in press.

Clift, P., Weiner, G. and Wilson, E (1981) *Record Keeping in Primary Schools.* London, Macmillan Education.

DES (1978) *Primary Education in England.* A survey by HM Inspectors of Schools. London, HMSO.

DES (1983) Science in Primary Schools. A discussion paper produced by the HMI Science Committee. London, DES.

DES (1985) Science 5 to 16: a Statement of Policy. London, HMSO.

DES (1987) A *Report. National Curriculum Task Group on Assessment and Testing.* London, DES and Welsh Office.

Harlen, W. (1997) Primary teachers' understanding in science and its impact in the classroom. *Research in Science Education,* 27 (3) 323–338.

Harlen, W., Holroyd, C. and Byrne, M. (1995) *Confidence and Understanding in Teaching Science and Technology in Primary Schools.* Scottish Council for Research in Education. Edinburgh.

Harris, S. with Keys, W. and Fernandes, C. (1997*) Third International Mathematics and Science Survey. Third National Report. Achievement in Mathematics and Science Practical Activities at Age 13 in England.* Slough, NFER.

There are also three Scottish TIMSS Reports:
Achievements of Secondary1 and Secondary 2 Pupils in Mathematics and Science
Achievements of Primary 4 and Primary 5 Pupils in Mathematics and Science *and Assessment of Practical Skills in Mathematics and Science.* http://www.hmis. scotoff.gov.uk

Nuffield Primary Science (1995) Teachers' Guides, Pupils' Books and Co-ordinators' Handbook. London, Collins Educational.

SPACE (Science Processes and Concepts Exploration) Research Reports. *Evaporation and Condensation* (1990), *Growth* (1990), *Light* (1990), *Sound* (1990), *Electricity* (1991), *Materials* (1991), *Processes of Life* (1992), *Rocks, Soil and Weather* (1992), *Forces,* (1998). Liverpool University Press.

Schilling, M., Hargreaves, L., Harlen, W., with Russell, T. (1990) *Assessing Science in the Primary Classroom: Written Tasks,* London, Paul Chapman Publishing.

1.4 Science for All

Michael J. Reiss

Pupils differ with respect to such characteristics as gender, ethnicity, class, the extent to which they may have special needs, their preferred learning styles and other aspects of their personality and home culture. Not only do pupils differ in all sorts of ways, but you, their teacher, will have differing expectations of them from your previous knowledge of pupils.

What is a science teacher to do with this diversity? Teaching to match pupils' differences in ability are discussed in Chapter 3.5 on Differentiation. This chapter argues that to take account of other aspects of this diversity leads to teaching that is both just and a better form of science education. I begin by asking two questions: 'To what extent do we need to provide different curricula, resources and teaching approaches for different categories of pupils?' and 'Do we present some pupils with an understanding of science that makes them feel it is not for them?' After a review of relevant policy statements, I examine practical work, the use of narrative, language issues, assessment issues and how to challenge racist, sexist and other discriminatory behaviours. Finally, I look at possible ways to teach the topics Materials and Food.

To What Extent do we Need to Provide Different Curricula, Resources and Teaching Approaches for Different Categories of Pupils?

Should the same resources be provided for a pupil with a physical disability (such as severe sight impairment) and a pupil without such a disability? Of course not. But should both pupils receive exactly the same curriculum? This question is a harder one. And what of girls and boys? Should they receive identical teaching approaches? Some people argue 'No', others 'Yes'. I will discuss these questions below. Here it is sufficient to state the two fundamental *criteria* by which such questions will be answered, namely a combination of what is in each pupil's best interests and what is fair. Both criteria are needed: it might be in an individual pupil's best interests to hog a teacher's attention but that wouldn't be fair to the other pupils.

Do we Present some Pupils with an Image of Science that Makes Them Feel it is Not for Them?

Throughout the UK primary age range, pupils' enthusiasm for science remains high. During secondary schooling, though, it falls off sharply in physics and chemistry (Osborne, Driver and Simon, 1998). One very positive feature of the last fifteen years or so has been the extent to which professional associations such as the ASE, textbook authors and publishers, individual teachers and other science education professionals have taken on board issues to do with equality (Peacock, 1991; Thorp, 1991; Cobern, 1996; Guzzetti and Williams, 1996). Pupils are now exposed to far less bias with regard to the nature of science than was the case until recently. No longer is it implicitly assumed that physics is largely an activity carried out by white middle-class men with a penchant for rocket design. Pupils are less likely nowadays to be asked to tackle questions on 'The digestion of a ham sandwich' (inappropriate for Jews, Muslims, vegetarians and vegans).

Policy Statements

Many organisations, in the UK and elsewhere, have produced policy statements relevant to the notion of science for all. The ASE policy on 'Gender and Science Education' includes the following recommendations:

- *Teaching and learning styles should explore and build upon the personal experiences of learners of both sexes, and provide compensatory experiences to avoid reinforcing existing bias;*
- *Assessment schemes should support equal opportunities policies, enabling all young people to recognise their own strengths and weaknesses and thus to influence their own learning. Greater emphasis on formative and diagnostic assessment will contribute to and enhance this aspect of teaching and learning;*
- *Resources and displays of learners' work should reflect the principles developed in equal opportunities policies Display and other materials should ensure that stereotypical views relating to adult roles and to aptitude and ability in science are not reinforced. Opportunities should be provided for girls and boys to interact with women and men in employment areas with a scientific and technological base. Both traditional and non-traditional roles should be represented. Role models in the form of secondary sources about the place of women in science in past ages should also be promoted.* (ASE, 1997a)

A number of these recommendations about gender are echoed in the Association's policy on 'Race, Equality and Science Education' which also adds its own perspectives:

The science curriculum should emphasise that:

- *science is not neutral; scientists and the pursuit of science are influenced by the environment in which they operate;*

35

- *people from all societies now and in the past have been involved in scientific exploration and discovery;*
- *there is an interplay between science, technology and society;*
- *there is no scientific or genetic evidence to support racism.*

The teaching and learning of science should:

- *promote a study of the nature of science;*
- *encourage the teaching of process skills and the exploration of attitudes;*
- *help learners to question the reasons underlying the inequalities between peoples and nations, and relate such issues to those of global interdependence;*
- *question and challenge racist attitudes and assumptions;*
- *provide positive images and avoid stereo types of people, places and times;*
- *show science as a world-wide human activity;*
- *encourage a global awareness of environmental issues;*
- *build on the cultural background and experiences of learners;*
- *provide specific support for the language development of bilingual learners.*
  (ASE, 1997b)

Finally, the Association's policy on 'Access to Science Education' addresses issues that follow from the fact that pupils arrive at science lessons with different levels of physical, sensory, cognitive and emotional development:

Learners can be isolated by sensory physical, cognitive and emotional problems. Choosing familiar contexts and providing appropriate activities motivates and stimulates learners.

Appropriate science experiences will involve:

- *using a range of teaching and learning strategies*
- *developing concepts and skills gradually*
- *matching the demands of the activity to the learner*
- *allowing different outcomes for different individuals*
- *building on the learner's strengths*
- *allowing time for learners to reflect on their work*
- *using a range of methods to monitor progress*
- *ensuring written material is at an appropriate level for each learner*
- *explaining new vocabulary*
- *using first hand examples to reinforce understanding*
- *using a range of communication methods*
- *adopting a consistent presentation style for written work*
- *ensuring safe working conditions*
- *making effective use of learning support assistants.* (ASE, 1997c)

Exemplification of Practice

The intention of this section is to suggest some general guidelines, with examples, on:

- practical work
- the use of narrative
- language issues
- assessment issues
- challenging racist, sexist and other discriminatory behaviours
- suggestions for how to teach topics on Food and Materials.

Many of the suggestions here are appropriate whatever the composition of the classes you teach. Even if the pupils in a class are all of one gender, ability, ethnic group, class, personality, home language, sexual orientation and religion their science teaching can still be varied and interesting!

Practical Work

Practical work rightly lies at the heart of school science education. As every teacher is aware, girls and boys often interact differently with their teachers. Girls are more likely to ask for help or reassurance about what to do next. Teachers may accept girls' dependence on them, tell them what to do and thus reinforce feelings of relative helplessness (Murphy, 1991). Boys may get more attention than girls, at least partly because teachers spend time with them attempting to ensure that they don't misbehave, get injured or damage equipment. However, to every generalisation there is at least one exception. Precisely because some teachers strive to be fair to girls, some silent boys can go for months without ever having a science teacher spend any time with them at all (Reiss, in press).

When arranging practical work for pupils with special educational needs, including pupils with severe learning difficulties, it often helps to break down practical activities into small steps. At the same time, consider how apparatus or other facilities in a laboratory can be modified to provide the maximum opportunity for relevant practical work. For further details and excellent case studies see NCC (1992) and Jones (1993).

Ensure that some practical investigations are open-ended and connect with the real world (Woolnough, 1994). This helps pupils to own what they are doing, to work at their own pace and to involve themselves in their work. Project work (e.g. on astronomy topics) and problem-solving (e.g. 'How can we get a tennis ball to bounce up to nearly the height it was dropped from?') can engage pupils, particularly when such work begins with children's own ideas and interests.

An attractive working environment can work wonders. Get some plants and a couple of aquaria. Have some displays of pupils' work – not just posters and children's writing but interactive displays and on-going projects in all the areas of science. Ensure that such displays value what pupils have done, encourage them to question further and reflect linguistic and cultural diversity.

The Use of Narrative

Tell your pupils some of the wonderful stories about scientists in action. This helps to provide a broader image of science and can challenge stereotypes. It also allows meaningful links to be made with the history and geography curriculum. Include both details of the science these scientists did and of their personal lives. For example:

- Lewis Howard Latimer (1848–1928) was an African–American scientist born six years after his father had escaped from slavery by fleeing from his masters. When Edison invented the electric light bulb in 1879, the bulbs only lasted a week. Latimer developed bulbs that could burn for months. He received patents for his inventions and became the chief designer for the installation of electric lights in Canada, New York and Philadelphia. His company sent him to London to set up an Electric Light Department. In London he met with much racial prejudice. He continued his work in London because of his faith in a just God and a belief that black people should set an example of excellence wherever they found themselves.

- China has always experienced earthquakes. Such earthquakes were often the trigger for food riots or attempts at rebellion. The government had every reason for wanting to know as soon as possible of any earthquakes in distant provinces. In 132 CE (BCE 'Before the Common Era' and CE 'Common Era' are often used in preference to the Christian BC 'Before Christ' and AD 'Anno Domini') Chang Heng, Astronomer Royal during the later Han Dynasty, unveiled his seismograph earthquake detector. Almost 2 m in diameter and made of bronze, it consisted of a series of dragons' heads attached to a central flask. Each dragon held in its mouth a delicately poised ball. Beneath each dragon was a frog with an open mouth. The signal for an earthquake was the falling of one of the balls into its waiting frog. Understandably, court officials expressed considerable scepticism. The official historian of the day tells how they were convinced:

  > On one occasion, one of the dragons let fall a ball from its mouth though no perceptible shock could be felt. All the scholars at the capital were astonished at this strange effect occurring without any evidence of an earthquake to cause it. But several days later a messenger arrived bringing news of an earthquake in Lung-Hsi [about 700 kilometres to the North- West]. Upon this everyone admitted the mysterious power of the instrument. (cited in Temple, 1991, p 163)

- Caroline Herschel (1750–1848) was a German who came to England with her brother, William, in 1772. William's hobby was astronomy and together they embarked on a systematic survey of the entire night sky, making their own telescope for the project. At first Caroline had little enthusiasm for the survey, but in 1781 William discovered the planet we now know as Uranus and the two of them moved to a new home. Here Caroline became increasingly involved in astronomy. In 1783 she discovered three new nebulae (galaxies of stars), but it was only when William was away from home that she had the chance to work on her own. It was during such times over the period 1786 to 1797 that she discovered a total of eight comets. In 1787 she was granted an official salary by the king. As Caroline wrote, *the first money I ever in all my lifetime thought myself to be at liberty to spend to my own liking* (cited in Alic, 1986, p 129). She continued to work throughout her long life, dying at the age of 97 and being buried with a lock of William's hair. Caroline Herschel received many international awards and accolades and she and Mary Somerville, a Scottish writer on science, became the first women to be made honorary members of the Royal Society.

- The story of the Chipko Movement is an inspiring example of how a group of women have peacefully collaborated to stop the destruction of forests in their region and start a major tree-planting programme. The forests of the Himalayas are very important to the villagers who live in the foothills. These villagers depend on the trees for such things as firewood for cooking, fodder for their animals and a source of building materials. However, the slow growing sal, deodar and oak are highly prized commercially and much of the forest has been felled for non-local exploitation.

Without these trees, the humus that acts as a sponge and absorbs the monsoon rains is scarcer. In consequence, floods are more frequent and heavier, and erosion and landslides have become serious problems. On 20 July 1970, a fierce storm struck the Alaknanda valley and in the resulting flood there were many deaths. Relief workers and local people organised marches following the Gandhian tradition of non-violent protest, and demanded the cessation of commercial logging and the return of forest control to local people.

Despite all this, commercial logging continued and in March 1974 the women organised vigilante parties to keep watch for any axemen. When axemen approached a tree, the women would surround and embrace the trees, protecting them. 'Chipko' means 'embrace' and so the Chipko Movement was born. Hundreds of women took a pledge to save the trees at the cost of their lives. Over the next few years auctions to sell off areas of land for logging had to be cancelled and the forests were saved. Subsequently the Chipko Movement began to afforest deforested areas with native species. Since 1981 the Movement has spread to other areas of India. For further details see the *Chipko Education Pack* produced by the Academy of Indian Dance (see 'Useful addresses' at the end of this chapter).

Pupils can be encouraged to write imaginatively. What would it be like to be Chang Heng, Caroline Herschel or a woman in the Chipko Movement? Then they can write about how they use science in their own lives and what they would like their biography to be if they had a career as a scientist. For further biographies of scientists and examples of how the history of science can be used to enrich science teaching. (See Solomon (1991), Ellis (1992) and Reiss (1993).)

Language Issues

There are four language skills: listening, speaking, reading and writing. Pupils can develop each of these in science. Here are some suggestions connected with our use of language that are worth bearing in mind:

- Talk and write in short sentences. Avoid unnecessary polysyllabic words.
- Take care with your handwriting on blackboards, whiteboards, OHTs, worksheets and when marking pupils' work.
- Explain all specialised or difficult vocabulary (e.g. 'concentration', 'food', 'force', 'subsequently') whether or not the word is specific to science. Take particular care with words that have more than one meaning (e.g. 'since').
- Write down specialised vocabulary and/or encourage pupils to keep a vocabulary book.
- Consider using boxes, arrows and standard logos (e.g. a pencil for 'Write here') instead of providing written information and instructions only in words.

- Encourage pupils to talk about science with one another in the language and terms they want (whether or not they are bilingual).
- Take care when using metaphors, similes or other models and introduce and explain them as such.
- Label shelves and cupboards where equipment is kept in the language(s) familiar to pupils. Pupils themselves can help provide these labels.
- Provide a copy of important instructions in each pupil's home language. Ensure that all writing intended for pupils is sufficiently large and clear to be visible – enlarging photocopiers can work wonders providing the original is clear enough.
- Ensure that all relevant oral contributions, whether by pupils or yourself, are audible and try to give all pupils space to speak.
- Consider enabling pupils to record their work using a word processor or on video or audio tapes.
- When setting reading tasks, ensure that what is being read is appropriate to the pupil. Get pupils to engage with their texts in a variety of ways. Usually this is done by getting pupils to provide written answers to questions. Other approaches include getting pupils to translate from one mode of communication into another (e.g. prose into diagrams) and to rewrite for a difference audience (e.g. a passage on teeth can be rewritten as if by a dentist providing information for patients).
- Keep alert to the possibility that some pupils would benefit from specialist equipment (e.g. glasses, hearing aids, Braille transcripts, pocket tape recorders).
- Liaise well in advance of lessons, even if only briefly, with language and other classroom assistants.

Assessment Issues

It is probably impossible to come up with a single assessment instrument that is universally fair to all pupils. For example, gender bias is accentuated by having science tests that are either all essays (generally favour girls) or all multiple choice (generally favour boys). The best practice is probably to adopt a range of assessment procedures. It is unfortunate, therefore, that in the interests of reliability, National Curriculum assessment in science currently uses such a narrow range of assessment instruments. Care also needs to be taken when setting and marking homework. While it is excellent practice to enable pupils to make use of their home environment, tasks that require access to books or home computers may severely disadvantage low-income families. (See Chapter 3.2).

Challenging Racist, Sexist and other Discriminatory Behaviours

There should be a whole-school policy on this and it should be followed. Any teacher, ideally any adult on school premises, should make it clear to the perpetrator of the discrimination, the person/people discriminated against and any onlookers or those in earshot at the time of the incident that such behaviour is completely unacceptable. In addition, any offending literature should be confiscated and graffiti quickly removed. If these procedures are adopted, and if your school has appropriate sanctions in place, discriminatory behaviours, including name calling, should be less frequent than otherwise. Good sex education and a good classroom climate can help reduce sexism, sexual harassment, racism and other sorts of unacceptable behaviour, for example towards pupils with disabilities. It is possible that science education could play a distinctive role in helping pupils scientifically to examine whether such discrimination is reasonable. Work on 'Ourselves' can afford opportunities for discussions about ways in which we are all similar as well as ways in which we differ from each other.

Materials

Here are some possible classroom activities for pupils to tackle when learning about materials:

- Identify the different materials in a classroom. Use/devise a key to identify these different materials (employ the full range of senses, e.g. wood and metal sound different when struck).
- A blindfolded child standing barefoot on tiles of various materials can try to guess what they are and choose which one they prefer. Pupils can then think what sorts of tiles are used for bathroom and kitchen floors and why these may be different.
- Research the range of materials used for making homes in different cultures. Why are different materials used? (Availability, different materials have different properties, tradition, etc.)
- Investigate the strengths of different types of fabric. How stretchy are they? The insulation of a beaker of warm water can be studied and related to clothing worn in cold weather. What other reasons determine the sorts of clothes we wear (including clothes worn by people with distinctive jobs, e.g. police officers, religious ministers)? Pupils can be shown, if they don't already know, how to weave and knit. If you get really enthusiastic you can keep silk worms, grow cotton and flax and visit sheep at shearing time.
- Make different types of paper including recycled paper. Why do people recycle paper?
- Use natural (e.g. from beetroot, grass and red cabbage) and artificial dyes to dye cloth.
- Investigate the properties of clay (e.g. permeability and hardness) before and after firing. Make coil pots and fire them outside in the pupils' own sawdust-burning kiln. (A kiln can be made form ordinary bricks without mortar, covered by an iron lid.)
- Relate jewellery design and manufacture to the properties of different materials.
- Visit a museum to see the historical uses of different materials for such things as jewellery, transport, weaponry (?) and drinking vessels.

Food

Here are some possible classroom activities for pupils to tackle when learning about food:

- Find out about the different ways different cultures preserve food (e.g. salting, drying, pickling, curing, cooking, freezing, canning, making into jam). Research into jam recipes and try making jam. What happens if the jam ends up too watery or is made without adding sugar? (Ensure that both girls and boys engage in any such practical activity.)

- List different foods eaten by pupils in the class. Find out where these foods come from (by looking at packets, asking parents, etc.) and produce a world map of where our food is grown. (Relate studies on food to studies on plant growth.) Carry out a survey to see how much of the cooking is done by different people in a family. Are all families the same?
- Keep food diaries to record which foods are eaten at what times of the day. (Relate to balanced diets but be careful to avoid culturally-specific judgements about what constitutes an inappropriate diet.)
- Make both unleavened and leavened 'breads'. Investigate factors that affect how much leavened bread rises.
- Research what leads to famines. What caused the Irish potato famine of 1845–9?
- Examine the place of food in different religious festivals (e.g. Eid, the Passover, Christmas, the Chinese New Year).

Concluding Remarks

There are two main reasons for ensuring that one's science teaching is 'Science for all'. One is that such teaching is just; the second is that such teaching is better science teaching. Two main things hold back some teachers from teaching in the ways advocated in this chapter. One is that such teaching requires a continual degree of reflection – 'Which pupils haven't I dealt with yet?', 'Are certain pupils dominating practical work?' The second is that if such teaching is something to which you aren't yet used, it requires a certain effort. One needs, for example, to learn about the contributions made by different cultures to science and to be firm in ensuring that all pupils in a class are treated fairly. However, such teaching is worth it!

About the Author

Michael J. Reiss is a senior lecturer in biology at Homerton College and a Priest in the Church of England. After a PhD and post-doctoral research in evolutionary biology, he taught in schools before returning to higher education. His research and writing interests are in science education, sex education and bioethics.

References and Further Reading

Alic, M. (1986) *Hypatia's Heritage: A History of Women in Science from Antiquity to the Late Nineteenth Century*. London, The Women's Press.

ASE (1997a) *Gender and Science Education: Policy*. Hatfield, ASE.

ASE (1997b) *Race, Equality and Science Teaching: Policy*. Hatfield, ASE.

ASE (1997c) *Access to Science Education: Policy*. Hatfield, ASE.

Cobern, W. W. (1996) Constructivism and non-western science education research. *International Journal of Science Education*, No 18, pp 295–310.

Ellis, P. (1992) *Science Changes!* Hemel Hempstead, Simon and Schuster.

Ghazi, T. (n.d.). Hadithi Nzuri: A Good Story. *Children's Literature from Africa, Asia and Latin America*. Chard, Somerset, Actionaid.

Guzzetti, B. J. and Williams, W. (1996) Gender, text and discussion: examining intellectual safety in the science classroom. *Journal of Research in Science Teaching*, No 33, pp 5–20.

Hellemans, A. and Bunch, B. (1989) *The Timetables of Science: A Chronology of the Most Important People and Events in the History of Science*. London, Sidgwick and Jackson.

Jones, A. (1993) *Science Education for Pupils with Special Needs*. Nottingham: Nottingham Trent University.

NCC (1992) *Curriculum Guidance 10: Teaching Science to Pupils withSpecial Educational Needs*. York, National Curriculum Council.

Osborne, J. F., Driver, R. and Simon, S. (1998*) Attitudes to science: issuesand concerns*. School Science Review.

Peacock, A. (Ed.) (1991*) Science in Primary Schools: The Multicultural Dimension*. Basingstoke, Macmillan Education.

Reiss, M. J. (1993) *Science Education for a Pluralist Society*. Buckingham, Open University Press.

Reiss, M. J. (In press) *Understanding Science Lessons*. Buckingham, Open University Press.

Solomon, J. (1991) *Exploring the Nature of Science*. Glasgow, Blackie.

Temple, R. (1991*) The Genius of China: 3000 Years of Science, Discovery and Invention*. London, Prion/Multimedia.

Thorp, S. (Ed.) (1991) *Race, Equality and Science Teaching: An Active INSET Manual for Teachers and Educators*. Hatfield, ASE.

Woolnough, B. E. (1994) *Effective Science Teaching*. Buckingham, Open University Press.

Useful Addresses

Academy of Indian Dance, 16 Flaxman Terrace, London WC1 9AT.

Access to Information on Multicultural Education, AIMER, Reading and Language Information Centre, University of Reading, Bulmershe Court, Earley, Reading RG6 1HE; Tel 01734 857123 extn 4871.

National Association for Gifted Children, Elder House, Milton Keynes MK9 1LR; Tel 01908 673677.

Oxfam, Oxfam House, 274 Banbury Road, Oxford 0X2 7DZ; Tel 01865 311311.

Women into Science and Engineering, The Engineering Council, 10 Maltravers Street, London WC2R 3ER; Tel 0171 240 7891.

For a good web site about women in every field of science see: http://scienceweb.dao.nrc.ca/ca/women/

1.5 Science Education from a European Perspective

Joan Solomon

This chapter explores the differences and similarities in science education across Europe.

Can Science Education Really be Different?

Science is an international endeavour; it is almost an ethic of science that it will ignore differences of nationality, creed and race in those who contribute to its work. Apart from during the period of the Second World War young scientists have always been free to study first in one European university and then in another, and they found the research being done in their field both complementary and continuous. They all read then, and still do, the same scientific journals. With that in mind it is not surprising to find that the content of the science curriculum is effectively the same in almost all the countries of Europe, especially in the secondary schools. Pupils everywhere have to learn about photosynthesis and Ohm's Law, the Periodic Classification of the elements, and all the other great ideas of science. There is some variation in the age at which they meet the different topics because of variations in the number of lessons given, when they start school, and the amount of choice and specialisation that pupils are allowed. These variations depend on several very broad factors:

- the perceived *purposes* of science education
- the national attitude to how *school education* should be carried out
- the national attitude towards *science as a system of thought*.

National curricula rarely stipulate exactly *how* science lessons are to be conducted in the schools, although they offer advice on the subject (and inspect rather less than in England!) and this is clearly crucial to the formation of pupils' attitudes towards science. Not only is the conduct of lessons affected by the teachers' perceptions of the nature of science as a system of thought – abstract and mathematical, or empirical and technical – it will also depend on educational traditions, such as whether children should be positively encouraged to co-operate in their study, and what is a suitable activity for a school teacher to perform (in France, Italy and many other countries no supervisory duties are carried out by secondary teachers).

A curious factor is the way that the boundaries of 'science' change from country to country. In Portugal, for example, Social Science, History and Geography are all included under the heading 'Science', and in France, Science and Mathematics are taught together in the upper secondary school. While the overall content learnt by pupils is generally unchanged by variations in these subject boundaries, attitudes towards 'science' may well be affected.

The Purposes of Education

The cultural diversity within Europe may be denser and richer than that in any other continent. First we may find quite general differences which affect broad *institutional factors in education* such as national and political attitudes towards:

- standardisation and uniformity (e.g. France)
- efficiency and market forces (e.g. UK)
- school autonomy (e.g. Sweden)
- a legal edict against labelling by ability (e.g. Denmark).

In addition there are differences in preferred *regulative principles of thought* which affect all education. These are naturally interesting to teachers since, without being mutually exclusive, they identify some very deep-seated motivations for education and for teaching, especially perhaps in science. They first arose as educational philosophies within Europe at different times and places, and the emphasis placed on each now varies from country to country. The major strands are called humanism, rationalism and naturalism.

Humanism

This focuses upon education for the formation of character. Sweden, and other Scandinavian countries, believe strongly that the purpose of education is to develop character and citizenship, just as the British public schools believe in developing character and leadership. Therein lies a substantial difference. While Swedish schools in the 1960s were already comprehensive and providing wide-ranging sex education for pupils according to their interpretation of the humanist precept, in our country other humanist arguments were still used to support grammar school selection to pick out able children and train them for the more responsible positions in society. Norwegian education, for example, favours small village schools which keep in close contact with their communities, while British educational authorities try to close small schools on the grounds of economics and lack of competition. Nevertheless both countries share a humanist vision of education's mission to cultivate the whole child – moral disposition as well as intelligence, and even bodily well-being, where that is thought to be connected with character.

Rationalism

This strand in European education is usually traced back to the philosopher Rene Descartes but it stands equally firmly in the tradition of mediaeval scholasticism. Here it is only the intellect of the child which is being trained, and not the character. In some ways, the French would argue, it leads to an 'egalite' in education which matches a deep principle in their national aspirations. It leads, however, to a curriculum of largely abstract topics, especially in mathematics and science, and an assessment method which is rigorous and positivist. Indeed the humanist educational systems mentioned before may look towards those of the rationalists with some envy. Who, after all, can hope to assess the character-forming objectives of a humanist system as rigorously as the logical ones of rationalism?

Sometimes selection by ability sits comfortably within rationalism since those who succeed in competitive examinations in school are likely to go on succeeding in them, and skill in the kind of problem-solving required in examinations is very easily equated with high intelligence when the latter is measured in a similar way. Teachers within this kind of system are also selected from amongst those who score well in degree examinations and are not thought to need much extra training, if any at all, before starting to pass on their science expertise to pupils. This sort of education is essentially a transmission process and teachers are *not* considered to be *in loco parentis*, as in the British system, nor burdened with responsibility for the moral development of their pupils. Thus it is only within the last ten years that France, Spain and Italy have required their science graduates to train at all before entering the teaching profession.

What is likely to work less well in the rationalist tradition is a mixed ability comprehensive system which still tries to teach in this tradition, as many of the modern French lycees are doing. This problem has been the subject of a recent OECD report and it results, in the worst cases, in *wild children and desperate teachers*. This is not because the system is marking out some children for a lower status, but because the curriculum, especially in Science and Mathematics, is intellectually demanding and presented in an abstract mode. French schools still teach Mathematics as the 'Queen of Sciences', usually avoid any discussion of social issues, and may offer their pupils limited practical work in the laboratory.

Linked with this intellectualism is the encyclopaedic tradition of the Enlightenment. In education this produces a tendency towards systematisation, which at its best makes for a wide respect for knowledge, and at its worst for rote learning.

Naturalism

The basic contrast between this tradition, and the other two mentioned, is that naturalist education is seen as an interior process, rather than one received (some of these radical educationalists might well have substituted the word *inflicted*) externally from school teachers. From Rousseau to Illitch, and William Morris to Pestalozzi and Steiner, there have been voices raised for the last two centuries which questioned whether the school as institution, with its top-down delivery of knowledge, was the right way to educate children. The argument still continues, but it should be stressed that if naturalism were no more than a radical de-schooling movement it would have no place in the educational literature. Its thinking is much more complex and constructive than this, and in some countries, such as Denmark, its influence is to be found right at the heart of school and college teaching.

Many of the themes that later naturalist educators developed were already to be found in Rousseau's *Emile* first published in 1762. These include respect for the 'natural state' of the child coupled with freedom to observe natural objects, a deep suspicion of all institutions including schools, and a dedication to the principle that children should make their own steps forward when they were ready to do so. The prime educational objective is the cultivation of creative thought.

The long continuing German debate about the nature of 'bildung' – education in the sense of 'forming the whole individual personality' – ensures that their educational systems are, at least in part, a nurturing process which brings out the inner potentiality of the child. In England the influence of Continental naturalism arrived late, and then came into conflict with H.E.Armstrong's more structured heuristic practical methods of teaching science. His account of *The Heuristic Method of Teaching, or the Art of Making Children Discover Things for Themselves* (1898), showed its distance from more radical naturalism by the use of the word *making*.

Naturalist approaches have always been a reaction against the formalism of school teaching. They are no longer confined by national frontiers because of their transformation and re-introduction from America in two successive waves during the present century. The earliest brought over were the ideas of John Dewey and focused on project work which is to be found all over Europe and is particularly strong in England and Denmark. The second wave brought the inspiring ideas of Jerome Bruner which included discovery learning.

Primary Science

Science is being taught in primary schools across almost all of Europe, and often by non-specialist teachers. Of course all the teacher educators bemoan the lack of scientific knowledge in their teachers, none more so than in the rationalist countries who have a vested interest in 'getting the concepts right'. These are the countries most likely to employ specialist teachers as early as possible (Poland and France). In terms of 'connectedness' it is the non-specialist teachers and the cross-curriculum teaching which is most likely to supply the transferability of scientific knowledge which lies at the root of popular culture. British pupils are the only ones to be assessed on their skills of investigations. In most other European countries the primary curriculum is less specific. Often practical investigations rarely take place at all, and no mention is made of topics in either physics or chemistry.

There is anxiety about how primary science is being taught. Most EU member states have decided that 'The Environment' is the most suitable topic for primary science. Sometimes it seems to comprise all of what is taught, and in countries such as Sweden and Spain, voices are questioning whether just feelings for animals and preserving the countryside might not be swamping out the teaching of scientific concepts. There is also worry in the more rationalist countries that 'Integrated Science' might be dissolving away the old science disciplines. Even the pun about school science *disintegrating* is common. Nevertheless science is usually much enjoyed by young children and this may provide a promising growth point for science as popular culture.

Practical Work and Technology

These are two ways in which British science education differs from that in most other European countries. We have compulsory assessed practical work and although many other countries exhort teachers to get their pupils to perform investigations, it does not happen regularly. The poorer countries, like Ireland and Greece, often blame this on to their lack of well-equipped laboratories but even when there is the latest apparatus, as in Germany, it may be used more for teachers' demonstrations than by the pupils, and mostly for rather routine practical work than for pupils' own investigations.

Finally there are unresolved controversies about the inclusion of what is variously called 'Technology' or 'Technics' in the school curriculum. In different European countries it may be:

- a study of the main *industrial means of production* (e.g. Italy) with or without a discussion of social effects
- only *Information Technology* and the use of computers
- acquisition of *workshop skills for the designing and making of technological artefacts* (e.g. the Netherlands, Denmark and the UK at junior secondary level).

In Poland and Italy technology is linked with physics. It is based within the science curriculum at various levels of secondary school in Greece, Denmark and the Netherlands. In Spain, Portugal, Belgium and the UK is it a separate subject. In Switzerland, Ireland, France and most German lander, technology does not figure at all for mainstream pupils except as IT. In Sweden technology now has all three of the meanings mentioned above, as a separate curriculum subject. Elsewhere it may be confined to a vocational stream.

Despite the English placing of Design and Technology as an important subject for all primary and secondary pupils, its natural successor – Engineering – is probably less popular here than in almost any other country. Our legacy of a humanistic view of education, as fitting children for their place in life, may have encouraged practical work only in the Victorian Trade Schools, and the 1944 Technical Schools, and that low status has dogged its progress ever since. Be that as it may, some Europeans look to our curriculum demands for Design and Technology with a rather inflated admiration. In Portugal and Hungary admiration may run the other way when we find that Engineering is the university goal of a large number of their school pupils and attracts almost as many girls as boys! (See Chapters 1.3 and 2.7.)

About the Author

Joan Solomon taught Science for more than 25 years. She became a PGCE Tutor at Oxford and carried out many commissioned research projects in both the UK and other European countries at primary and secondary levels. She is now Professor of Science Education at the Open University.

SECTION 2

Learning Science

2.1 Children's Learning of Science Concepts

Dorothy Watt

Over the last ten or so years, the dominant view in primary science has been that children learn best by behaving as scientists; using skills to develop their understanding of scientific concepts through investigation (see, for example, Harlen, 1985; 1993). This view clearly emphasises how children *learn* science and it has led to a much greater understanding of how learning occurs. The teachers' role has been to facilitate learning – not a passive role, but one in which teachers help children to behave scientifically and to interpret their findings. More recent developments suggest that giving the teacher a more active *teaching* role and broadening the range of classroom activities to include 'minds on' as well as 'hands-on' activities can lead to better learning for children. In this chapter, I begin by exploring what we know about how children learn and then consider how recent developments have addressed some of the challenges which investigative science poses for teachers and children when aiming to develop scientific understanding.

What Are Scientific Concepts?

In order to make sense of the world around us, we each have a mental 'store' in which our ideas and experiences are organised so that similar ones are grouped together. In such a group will be a general definition of the topic, some specific, related pieces of knowledge and an idea of the contexts in which it is applicable. These broad, organising groupings are known as concepts, and are an essential aspect of developing understanding.

Concepts can be of different sizes, and an example of one which organises a large number of ideas is that of a 'life cycle', which is illustrated in Fig 2.1A.

Life Cycle
- All living things pass through a number of stages during their life so that they can perpetuate their species.

Some examples of specific knowledge
- Caterpillars hatch out of eggs laid by butterflies.
- An apple will only grow if pollen reaches the right part of the apple blossom.
- Some human beings choose whether or not to reproduce.
- Flowering plants produce flowers and then seeds at the same time each year.
- When an organism reaches the end of its reproductive life, it begins to die.

Contexts
- Humans, tigers, rabbits, tomato, oak tree, fungi, etc. – all living things.

Fig 2.1A 'Life cycle' concept

Why Are Scientific Concepts Important?

The notion that all living things go through equivalent stages in order to perpetuate their species is a very powerful one in terms of explaining our world. Without it as an organising framework, frog spawn turning into tadpoles and trees flowering can seem to be interesting, but unrelated, events. We all know how frustrating it is to be made to learn isolated bits of information without anyone helping us see the wider picture. If we are to help children to make scientific sense of the world, we must help them to create this order by developing their own concepts so they can use specific information with understanding. Effectively, we are giving them a set of pegs on which to hang the coats, hats and scarves of science knowledge.

Concept Development and the National Curriculum

The programmes of study in the National Curriculum for Science (NC) at Key Stages 1 and 2 (DfEE, 1995) can be used to develop children's conceptual understanding. However, particularly at KS2, it is easy to see how the required experiences could be presented as pieces of information to be learnt. In fact, the level descriptions lean heavily towards knowledge and recall of correct nomenclature, and the National Standard Tests are even more weighted in that direction. Take, for example, 'Materials and their Properties' KS2, Pupils should be taught about the water cycle and the part played by evaporation and condensation. These ideas are assessed within the AT3 level 4 description by children's ability to, ...use scientific terms, such as evaporation or condensation, to describe changes. The Standard Test questions then test the children's ability to apply these scientific labels correctly, and children's understanding of the underlying processes seems to be unimportant. While isolated knowledge is far easier to teach, particularly for anyone who feels insecure in their own *understanding* of science, it is much harder for children to learn in a way that enables them to use the information meaningfully later on or in other contexts. That is, children can be developing a great collection of coats, etc. but without the pegs to hang them on. It is therefore important to consider approaches to teaching which enable children to develop a coherent conceptual framework so they become scientifically literate and able to use their science learning in everyday situations. (See Chapters 3.3 and 3.4.)

The Existence of Children's Ideas

As active, thinking beings, children are developing ideas from their daily experiences and forming concepts to help them understand events. Of course, there is no guarantee that children's scientific ideas and explanations will be in line with the accepted scientists' view and, because their experiences are limited and much of science runs counter to observations (e.g. forces in relation to movement), it is quite likely they will not be. Indeed, there is so much evidence for children's intuitive ideas that their existence is undisputed, and their characteristics have been identified as:

• common to children in different parts of the world

- hard to change because they make personal sense to children
- specific to particular contexts because of children's limited experiences.

So, for example, a child is more likely to have ideas about sound travelling in the context of talking through a string telephone than when hearing a rubber band twang, because the string makes a visible link between both speaker and listener. It is easy to see how children would be satisfied with their ideas which do not include an over-arching understanding that sound is *always* vibrations.

Early Approaches to Developing Children's Understanding

'Constructivist science' is a widely used phrase which is shorthand for a particular perspective on teaching and learning. Briefly, constructivist theories are characterised by the view that learners actively construct their own understanding from their experiences of the world. The most widely used constructivist theory in science education stated that children's ideas got in the way of school science learning and therefore needed 'conceptual change', so constructivist researchers and teachers developed approaches to encourage this process. That most commonly advocated in secondary schools was 'cognitive conflict' (Posner *et al*, 1982), in which children compared their ideas with the currently held scientists' view to see that their idea was less helpful at explaining phenomena across a range of contexts. Secondary school children are older and more able to handle abstract ideas relating to 'invisible' phenomena such as sound waves, than are primary school children. Harlen and Osborne (1985) developed a primary approach which takes account of the pupils' age and the fact that primary teachers are generalists, often without a science background. This approach started from children's existing ideas and encouraged them to engage in their own learning by testing them. The teacher was a facilitator, valuing their ideas and providing support and appropriate opportunities for scientific investigation.

The Primary SPACE Project

The main large-scale primary constructivist research project in the UK has been the SPACE (Science Processes and Concept Exploration) Project which has produced a wide range of research reports to describe its methods and findings (e.g. Osborne, Black, Smith and Meadows, 1990; Watt and Russell, 1990). This research was designed to be realistic in terms of what goes on normally in classrooms, and teachers were given a range of techniques to enable them to find out their children's ideas and to begin to develop these in a direction which was more scientifically useful. Below are listed the techniques for finding out and developing children's ideas, and comprehensive case studies of project activities can be found in each of the SPACE research reports. (See also Chapter 1.3.)

Finding Out Children's Ideas

- Free writing/drawing in a log book, allowing children to make entries over a period of time when they are considering topics such as 'growth' or 'evaporation' in which changes happen slowly and imperceptibly.
- Structured writing/drawing in response to a specific question to focus their thinking on a particular aspect of a phenomenon (see Fig 2.1B for an example).
- Completing a picture by adding relevant points such as the location of light to a picture in which the background has already been drawn.
- Individual discussion between a child and teacher. (See also Chapter 3.7.)

Helping Children Develop Their Ideas

- *Building on children's ideas through investigation*, posing questions for children to consider and providing opportunities for them to test out their ideas.
- *Testing the 'right' idea alongside the children's ideas*, providing opportunities for children to compare their explanation with that of scientists.
- *Making imperceptible changes perceptible*, finding ways of helping children realise that very slow changes, e.g. growing, do not only happen at night or when the children are not there, using evidence such as videos of time-lapse photography of plant growth.
- *Helping children to generalise* from one specific context to others by helping them to identify common features.
- *Refining children's use of vocabulary*, helping them to clarify particular terms, e.g. 'growing', and how these relate to, for example, 'stretching'.

These techniques, particularly investigation, clearly relate to Harlen and Osborne's (1985) primary constructivist approach. However, there is less emphasis on children's practical activity and more on the teacher taking an active role in concept development by promoting thinking. There is no sense in which these techniques signal a return to 'chalk and talk' as the children and teacher are actively involved in constructing understanding and working together towards the scientists' view. While the SPACE Project employed these techniques to help children to develop their own understanding, these approaches have subsequently been developed so that the scientists' views are more evident.

The following case study shows how one teacher approached the topic of 'sound' with a Y5 class. It is particularly useful because it shows how different strategies are used at different points in the topic to reinforce and develop the children's understanding, and how whole class discussion played a central role.

A Case Study

Veronica used the statements in the PoS for Physical Processes at KS2 to focus her teaching and assessments. These are:

> *Pupils should be taught:*
>
> 3e *that sounds are made when objects vibrate but that vibrations are not always directly visible;*

3f that the pitch and loudness of sounds produced by some vibrating
    objects can be changed;

3g that vibrations from sound sources can travel through a variety of
    materials to the ear.

The idea which is central to these statements is that of sound being linked to vibrations, and this can be seen as a recurring theme in Veronica's teaching.

Veronica began the topic by asking the children to draw their ideas about sound in the context of a drum and a rubber band. Fig 2.1B shows examples of the range of responses she received about the drum. They range from a child who provided the same explanation in both contexts and used the term 'vibration' consistently to a child who described what he could hear from the drum and see from the rubber band in completely context-dependent ways.

Veronica used her assessment of the children's drawings to assign them to particular group activities to develop their understanding of factors affecting sound production. For the three children whose ideas are in Fig 2.1B, the activities were:

a) *Investigate which factors alter the sound that can be made with an elastic band*, an investigation which is very open and makes high demands on procedural as well as conceptual understanding.

b) *Does a drum have to have a top and a bottom to make a noise?* This is an investigation which is far more closed with a clearly limited focus.

c) *Put some rice onto a drum and then hit the drum. Watch the rice very carefully. What is happening to it? Why is it happening?* This is an illustrative activity designed to focus observations onto the production of vibrations.

This session culminated in a class discussion which Veronica sequenced so that she was able to show the commonalities between the children's findings, for example that tightness or tension was an important factor, and to generate alternative words for 'vibrate' such as 'wobble' or 'shake' to check their understanding.

The following session proceeded similarly, with children being directed to activities Veronica thought would improve their science understanding, and one group again being given structured, illustrative activities to help them 'see' vibrations (salt on a cymbal, a tuning fork resting on water) as that idea was still eluding them. Again, concluding the class discussion was carefully sequenced and Veronica used the description and explanation of the illustrative activities to reinforce and refine the class definition of vibration:

T: *'Let's see what each group has found out this afternoon. We'll start with the first group. What was the first thing you did?'*
'We put salt on the cymbal.'
T: *'You put salt on the cymbal. Then what?'* Right from the start, T speaks rapidly and responds very fast to the children's replies.
'We hit it.'
T: *'Did it make a noise?'*
'Yes.'
T: *'What did the salt do?'*
'It jumped up.'
T: *'When did it stop?'*

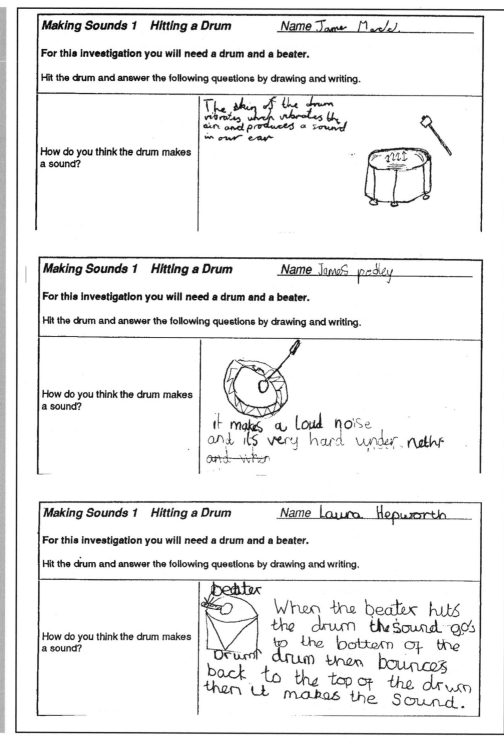

Making Sounds 1   Hitting a Drum   Name James Model.

For this investigation you will need a drum and a beater.

Hit the drum and answer the following questions by drawing and writing.

How do you think the drum makes a sound?

The skin of the drum vibrates which vibrates the air and produces a sound in our ear

---

Making Sounds 1   Hitting a Drum   Name James pedley

For this investigation you will need a drum and a beater.

Hit the drum and answer the following questions by drawing and writing.

How do you think the drum makes a sound?

it makes a loud noise and its very hard under. neath and when

---

Making Sounds 1   Hitting a Drum   Name Laura Hepworth

For this investigation you will need a drum and a beater.

Hit the drum and answer the following questions by drawing and writing.

How do you think the drum makes a sound?

beater

Drum

When the beater hits the drum the sound go's to the bottom of the drum then bounces back to the top of the drum then it makes the sound.

Fig 2.1B

'When the noise stopped.'

T: *'Can anyone tell us why?'* T addresses the whole class, then refocuses the request to the group who have done the demonstration, 'You tell us.'

'It's vibration.'

T: *'What's vibration?'* T looks to the whole class and hands are raised straight in the air. One person is selected to answer.

'Wobble.'

T: *'Is it slow or fast?'* Again, hands are raised and one is chosen.

'Fast.'

T: *'Can you make a sound without vibration?'*

'No.'

T: *'Then what did you do?'*

'We used a tuning fork.'

T: *'Show us what you did.'* A tuning fork is hit against the table then held against a piece of paper, which makes a buzzing sound. 'What's happening to the tuning fork on the paper?'

'It's vibrating.'

T: *'Vibrating?'* All arms are raised straight.

'Wobbling very quickly.'

(Watt, 1997; Session 3 lines 178–230)

By the sixth session, when children were exploring sound travelling, all of the children were able to use the term 'vibrate' correctly and in context, as well as being able to make general statements about the links between hard surfaces and echoes, and how tension is necessary in a string for sound to travel through it.

These activities demonstrate how a teacher can:

- *make imperceptible phenomena perceptible* by placing salt on a cymbal before hitting it, for example
- *help children to generalise* by using the contexts of a drum and a rubber band in the same lesson and making comparisons in the class discussion
- *refine children's use of vocabulary*, particularly the term 'vibration'
- *pose questions for children to consider* in light of their ideas about 'sound'.

In more general terms, the clear focus on key ideas meant that Veronica:

- helped children learn key concepts by focusing on them in science activities
- complemented the emphasis on 'hands-on' by promoting 'minds-on' activities to encourage children to think and develop concepts
- knew what ideas children were likely to have in order to develop ways of explaining concepts that children would understand
- accepted that children's ideas are useful for everyday life, but encouraged children to understand that thinking scientifically is different and requires them to use words in particular ways.

Challenges with Working from Children's Ideas

Children's ideas provide starting points for science which relate to everyday experiences, and which children can discuss in everyday language. The relevance of this, and having their ideas acknowledged and valued, is likely to contribute to children's enjoyment of science, thus improving motivation and making science teaching in the classroom easier to manage. These motivational aspects alone would make constructivism worth considering as an approach to teaching and learning science. However, it raises a number of significant issues in relation to the classroom context and expectations of both teachers and children about how teaching and learning happens.

Issues for Teachers

Valuing Children's Ideas

It can be difficult to ask for children's ideas, listen to them and accept them as valid – whether they are in line with the scientists' view or not. This acceptance of any response is at odds with the usual 'teacher' position of being in control of the right answer. My research suggests that, when teachers feel they cannot explicitly disagree with an idea, they use their tone of voice or a particular form of words (e.g. 'Does anyone agree with that?') to indicate their opinion to children (Watt, 1992; 1996). Judging the moment at which to move on from accepting ideas to, for example, helping children to learn new vocabulary and expecting them to use it appropriately is difficult and requires sensitivity and an awareness of both teaching goals and children.

Organising the Testing of Ideas

As the children's ideas are so interesting, there is an understandable desire to establish the idea of every child in the class and then to get each of them to test their own idea. This can cause real management problems, and is not the most productive approach. Firstly, the underlying science ideas from the whole class can usually be clustered into no more than three groups. Using the ideas in Fig 2.1B, those groups could be:

a) Children who seem to be aware of vibrations and can use them to explain sound production;
b) Children who seem to be aware of sound as an 'entity' which moves but are not describing vibrations;
c) children who seem to be aware of properties of sound producers but who do not relate these to sound generation.

Secondly, putting children with different ideas in a group is more successful than clustering those with similar views (Howe, 1995). This is because it is tempting for them confirm their preferred idea, whereas disagreement between children is more likely to foster conceptual development by, for example, focusing observations on relevant features such as vibrations.

Issues for Children

Reinforcing Their Ideas

Because children's ideas are not usually the centre of the teaching process, asking for and accepting these can seem to be reinforcing them, actually making concept development harder. Spending only the necessary time establishing children's ideas and then focusing on the understanding to be developed (rather than asking children to develop their own ideas) should help children to focus on learning science.

Controlling Their Own Learning

While children's ideas are interesting, and children enjoy being asked about them, they do not expect to be in charge of developing their own understanding in school. Just as covert signals indicate which answers teachers agree with, so children look out for these subtle signs because they are used to being provided with the right answers. Being clear about learning intentions and key concepts makes the framework for learning explicit and enables children to take an active part in developing their science concepts through discussion and activity. Similarly, unless the children are involved in changing unspoken classroom rules related to working procedures, they are likely to behave as they have always done (Watt, 1997; White, 1988). For example, if children have been trained that they must always produce their neatest work, asking them for a quick sketch of their plans or ideas may still result in painstaking work, slowing the pace of the session.

Learning the Accepted Science View

When children learn science by testing their ideas there is no guarantee that any new understanding will be nearer to the scientific view. However, the NC requires that children acquire particular knowledge and understanding so the constructivist approach which, in theory, enables children to reach a more scientific view by finding their own ideas inadequate, can, in practice, turn into an inefficient guessing game, with the teacher still knowing the right answers and children having to work these out through investigation. A clear focus on key ideas and intentions for learning, as Veronica had, removes the element of guessing while still encouraging discussion of meaning.

Over-emphasis on Practical Activity

An area of understanding such as 'sound' is pretty amenable to first-hand exploration and activity, even though primary science investigations are very hard to do accurately. However, not all phenomena can be explained through observable features. Air, for example, is not mentioned as a requirement for life in the Programme of Study at either KS 1 or 2, presumably because it can neither be seen nor adequately removed for 'proof' of its importance to be experimentally determined. Such over-reliance on practical activity reduces science to 'learning by doing' when this is not always the most efficient approach to developing understanding. Even very young children can do 'mind experiments', trying things out in their imagination, and it can foster the creativity we value as a scientific attitude. Simple modelling of, for example, dissolving through drama can positively enhance understanding beyond the observable – making imperceptible phenomena perceptible.

Current Approaches to Developing Children's Understanding

Children's ideas seem very attractive as a starting point for developing their conceptual understanding. However, we have an obligation to give children access to the 'big ideas' of science, so we need to think about how we *teach* science as well as how children *learn* it. This involves a subtle change in the way children's ideas might be used. Expecting children to subject their ideas to systematic testing can lead to conceptual development in unanticipated and unhelpful directions. Their ideas can be used by the teacher to identify what they know and to ascertain what they will still need to learn. Teaching can be aimed towards bridging the gap.

It is easy to think of examples in which everyday language leads towards unscientific notions – the sun going behind a cloud, for example, which suggests that the sun is moving when in fact the clouds are being blown in front of it. Children therefore need to learn to use language in two ways, depending on whether they are involved in science or conversing in everyday life.

However, because children's ideas are so often tied in to how we use language in everyday life, attempting to remove the ideas altogether could disadvantage children socially. Imagine a child who is asked to shut the door to stop the cold getting in, retorting that it is not the cold getting in but the heat which is moving out! Taken to its absurd conclusion, it would obviously be unhelpful for the fluent development of children's everyday idiomatic language. Instead, helping children to see that science learning is something special and often different, would mean them learning when it is appropriate to use everyday ideas and when science knowledge should provide the framework for thinking and talking. This position is consistent with Solomon's (1983) proposal that children's ideas should be acknowledged, while science learning should be regarded as a distinct process.

This approach has its own challenges, not least of which is the understanding of the science required to teach it effectively. However, Veronica was not a science specialist. She was supported in her teaching by well-structured curriculum materials which focused on the key concepts children need to develop and linked these explicitly to particular activities, either practical or discussion-based. This ensured that the children could move forward even when teachers lack confidence in the necessary science concepts.

Summary

The following statements summarise our current understanding of how to teach for scientific concept development:
- there is a body of scientific concepts to which children are entitled to have access
- we need to help children develop coherent science concepts
- we need a range of active approaches for constructing understanding
- children have their own everyday ideas about science which we should acknowledge.

But:

- encouraging children to test their own ideas as the principal way of developing their own understanding can be inefficient and misleading
- helping children to recognise scientific thinking as separate from everyday thinking may be more helpful than trying to change their ideas.

About the Author

Dorothy Watt is a lecturer in primary science education at the London University Institute of Education. She is particularly interested in effective teaching and learning in primary science, with a focus on classroom interaction.

References

Department for Education (1995). *Science in the National Curriculum*. London, HMSO.

Harlen, W. (Ed) (1985) *Primary Science: taking the plunge*. London, Heinemann.

Harlen, W. (1993) *Teaching and learning primary science* (2nd ed.). London, Paul Chapman.

Harlen, W. and Osborne, R. (1985). A model for learning and teaching applied to primary science. *Journal of Curriculum Studies*, Vol 2, No17, pp 133–146.

Howe, C. (1995) Learning about physics through peer interaction. In P. Murphy, M. Sellinger, J. Bourne and M. Briggs (Eds) *Subject Learning in the Primary Curriculum*. pp 197–204. London, Routledge.

Osborne, J., Black, P., Smith, M. and Meadows, J. (1990) *Primary SPACE Project Research Report: Light*. Liverpool, Liverpool University Press.

Posner, G. J., Strike, K. A., Hewson, P. W. and Gertzog, W. A. (1982). Accommodation of a scientific conception: toward a theory of conceptual change. *Science Education*, Vol 2, No 66, 211–227.

Solomon, J. (1983). Learning about energy: how pupils think in two domains. *European Journal of Science Education*, Vol 1, No 5, pp 49–59.

Watt, D. and Russell, T. (1990) *Primary SPACE Project Research Report: Sound*. Liverpool, Liverpool University Press.

Watt, D. (1992) An evaluation of the impact of selected in-service activities on teacher questioning behaviours in constructivist primary science education. Unpublished MEd thesis, University of Liverpool.

Watt, D. (1997) Towards effective teaching in primary science: an analysis of the evolving contribution of the SPACE Project to understanding the role of the teacher. Unpublished PhD thesis, University of Warwick.

White, R. (1998) *Learning Science*. Oxford, Blackwell.

Further Reading

Perspectives on Effective Teaching

Bennett, N. (1989) Changing perspectives on teaching–learning processes in the post-Plowden era. In Murphy, P. and Moon, B. (Eds) *Developments in learning and assessment* (pp 224–236). London, Hodder and Stoughton.

Carre, C. and Ovens, C. (1994) *Science 7–11: developing primary teaching skills*. London, Routledge.

Osborne, J. and Simon, S. (1996) Primary Science: past and future directions. *Studies in Science Education*, No 27, pp 99–147.

Osborne, J. and Simon, S. (1996) *Teacher subject knowledge: implications for teaching and policy*. British Educational Research Association Annual Conference.

Nott, M. and Wellington, J. (1996) When the black box springs open: practical work in schools and the nature of science. *International Journal of Science Education*, Vol 7, No 18, pp 807–818.

Sutton, C. (1992) *Words, Science and Learning*. Buckingham, Open University Press.

Children's Ideas and Constructivism

Driver, R. and Erickson, G. (1983) Theories in action: some theoretical and empirical issues in the study of students' conceptual frameworks in science. *Studies in Science Education*, 10, pp 37–60.

Engel Clough, E. and Driver, R. (1986) A study of consistency in the use of students' conceptual frameworks across different task contexts. *Science Education*, Vol 4, No 70, pp 473–496.

Johnson, P. and Gott, R. (1996) Constructivism and evidence from children's ideas. *Science Education*, Vol 5, No 80, pp 561–577.

Osborne, R. and Freyberg, P. (Eds) (1985) *Learning in science: the implications of children's science*. London, Heinemann.

Osborne, R. and Wittrock, M. C. (1983) Learning science: a generative process. *Science Education*, Vol 4, No 67, pp 489–504.

Scott, P., Asoko, H. and Driver, R. (1991) Teaching for conceptual change: a review of strategies. In R. Duit, F. Goldberg, and H. Neidderer (Eds), *Research in physics learning; theoretical issues and empirical studies* (pp 310–329). Kiel.: University of Kiel.

Critiques of Constructivism

O'Loughlin, M. (1992) Rethinking science education: beyond Piagetian constructivism towards a sociocultural model of teaching and learning. *Journal of Research in Science Teaching*, No 29, pp 791–820.

Solomon, J. (1994) The rise and fall of constructivism. *Studies in Science Education*, No 23, pp 1–19.

2.2 Learning to Investigate

Anne Goldsworthy

This chapter reports on some of the findings from the AKSIS Project. It categorises the different types of investigation carried out by teachers, considers what pupils are currently learning through investigative work and identifies some of the problems encountered in the classroom. It also offers some suggestions for improving pupils' performance.

Most teachers will agree that investigations are the hardest part of the science curriculum to manage. Coping with a large class of 30 or more pupils carrying out practical work is difficult enough; but when teachers want to give them a degree of autonomy as well, it can seem a very hard task indeed. Few other countries ask their primary teachers to carry out investigations where pupils have such a degree of independence. Our curriculum asks a lot of primary teachers and their pupils.

How are teachers coping with the demands of investigative work? How are pupils responding? What is the range of investigations that pupils carry out? What are successful strategies for teaching investigations? These are some of the issues addressed by the AKSIS (ASE/King's College Science Investigations in Schools) Project.

In order to find out what was happening in school science investigations, the AKSIS Project worked closely with thirty-four teachers from Key Stages 2 and 3. They recorded detailed information about an investigation, both before and after the event. The data included samples of pupils' written work, a pupil questionnaire, and, in many cases, video-tapes of the lessons. The teachers also attended weekend conferences and elaborated on their written records through taped individual interviews and group discussions. The AKSIS teachers were volunteers and they cannot, therefore, be considered a representative sample. However, their records give an indication of what is happening in science investigation lessons and evidence of some successful teaching strategies.

The Current Picture

What Type of Investigations Are Carried Out?

Investigations can come in many forms but the AKSIS teachers suggested two features that they have in common. Firstly, in investigative work, pupils have to make their own decisions: they must be given some autonomy at some stage about how the investigation is carried out. Secondly, an investigation must require pupils to use some investigational procedures such as planning investigations, measuring, observing, analysing data and evaluating results. Working from this definition of an investigation, the AKSIS team has categorised investigations into six different types.

1) Fair Testing

These investigations are concerned with exploring relations between variables or factors. It is described in the Key Stage 2 Programme of Study (DFE 1995) as 'changing one factor and observing or measuring the effect, whilst keeping other factors the same'.
    Examples:

- What affects the rate at which sugar dissolves?
- Which paper towel soaks up most water?

2) Classifying and Identifying

Classifying is a process of arranging a large range of objects or events into manageable sets. Identifying is a process of recognising objects and events as members of particular sets, possibly new and unique sets, and allocating names to them.
    Examples:

- Which things float and which things sink?
- What is that tree?

3) Pattern Seeking

These investigations involve observing and recording natural phenomena or carrying out surveys and then seeking patterns in the findings.
    Examples:

- Do dandelions in the shade have longer leaves than those in the light?
- Do people with longer legs jump higher?

4) Exploring

Pupils either make careful observations of objects or events, or make a series of observations of a natural phenomenon occurring over time.
    Examples:

- How does frog spawn develop over time?
- What happens when different liquids are added together?

5) Investigating Models

These are investigations that explore models and are more likely to be found in Key Stages 3 and 4 than in Key Stages 1 and 2.
    Example:

- Will copper increase or decrease in mass during combustion?

6) Making Things or Developing Systems

These investigations are usually technological in nature, but have a high scientific content.

Examples:

- Can you find a way to design a pressure pad switch for a burglar alarm?
- How could you make a weighing machine out of elastic bands?

Fig 2.2A shows the number of each different type of investigation carried out by AKSIS teachers:

Type of Investigation	Number of Examples (n = 34)
Fair Testing	26
Classifying and Identifying	4
Pattern Seeking	2
Exploring	0
Investigating Models	0
Making Things or Developing Systems	2

Fig 2.2A Investigations carried out by AKSIS teachers

Fair Testing investigations were carried out by three quarters of AKSIS teachers. Although Fair Testing is an important way of getting evidence, these results indicate that most pupils rarely encounter other types of investigation. There are also some schools where Fair Testing is the only type of investigation that pupils meet. Another consequence of the domination of Fair Testing investigations is, that on some occasions, other types of investigation are tackled as if they have the same structure as fair tests. For example, in a Y3 investigation pupils were asked to sort materials into those that were attracted to a magnet and those that were not. This was a Classifying investigation. However, because the teacher assumed it was a Fair Testing investigation, the pupils were asked how they would make it fair. Unsurprisingly, they had some difficulty responding to the question.

What are Pupils Learning from Investigations? What Are the Problems?

Planning Investigations

Amongst the AKSIS investigations were several examples where pupils offered ideas for investigation. For example, pupils in a Y6 class suggested what might affect the swing of a pendulum and some Y3/4 pupils offered several factors which might affect the time taken for a parachute to fall. In general, most pupils doing 'Fair Testing' investigations were able to plan what to do by routinely changing one factor, whilst keeping all others the same. It was less apparent that pupils were aware of the reasons for controlling variables in this way.

In some instances teachers thought they were *allowing the pupils to make more decisions* than was the case. A Y4 investigation into the effects of different types of exercise on pulse rate was one of the more open investigations of the project, with groups of pupils following up their own ideas about what and how to investigate. For example, one group of pupils used the same pupil to run, skip, walk and jump; whilst another group compared the pulse rate of four different pupils after they had walked, skipped, laughed and rested. However, a breakdown of the decisions taken about the investigation shows that even in this investigation, which the teacher considered to be open-ended, many of the decisions were, in fact, taken by her (see Fig 2.2B).

Decision to take	What was decided	Who took decision
Independent variable or what we change	Type of exercise	Teacher
Categories of independent variable	Running/skipping/ walking/laughing, etc.	Pupils
Size of sample (no. of people tested)	1–4	Pupils
Dependent variable or what we measure	Pulse rate (beats per minute)	Teacher
Equipment used to measure	Stethoscope (to aid counting of heart beats)	Teacher
Control variables or what we keep the same	i) person ii) time spent exercising iii) time spent resting	Pupils
Value of control variables	i) member(s) of group ii) from 1 to 3 minutes iii) from 1 to 3 minutes	Pupils

Fig 2.2B Planning decisions table

Teachers need to find a balance between allowing pupils to make their own planning decisions, whilst supporting them enough to enable them to plan an investigation which yields worthwhile evidence. If teachers are clear about which procedures the investigation aims to teach, they will find it easier to identify which planning decisions their pupils should take. It is often unrealistic, and impractical, to expect pupils to make all the planning decisions needed for an investigation.

Obtaining Evidence

In some instances, where pupils had access to suitable measuring instruments, they were able to use them to make measurements. For example, in the pulse rate investigation Y4 pupils were able to measure the pulse rate reasonably accurately because the teacher supplied stethoscopes which she had previously taught the pupils how to use. Another class of Y6 pupils successfully used newtonmeters (forcemeters) to measure the force needed to start an object moving and hence the force of friction.

Where difficulties occurred, they were often as a result of practical problems. An extreme example was when a Y6 group of pupils ended up measuring distance inaccurately, with a line of metre sticks, because another teacher took away their tape measure to use in a PE lesson. In another Y6 investigation into pendulums, the pupils altered factors, such as the mass or the length of string, and counted the number of swings before the pendulum came to rest. The pupils found it extremely hard to judge when the pendulum had finally stopped swinging and the number of swings was sometimes very large, up to 525 swings. Although these pupils had planned well and tackled the investigation with considerable perseverance, the difficulty they had counting the number of swings caused some groups to have erratic and unreliable results. As the teacher's aims for the lesson focused on fair testing and the recording and presenting of evidence, she would have been quite justified in intervening and telling the pupils how to measure the number of swings more effectively, for example by counting the number of swings in a minute. In her desire to leave all decisions to the pupils, some groups ended up with meaningless results.

Considering Evidence

A clear trend that emerged from the AKSIS investigations, was that teachers and pupils spend considerably less time considering evidence, than on planning and carrying out the investigation. Also, it was quite rare to find teachers who had explicitly taught the skills needed to consider evidence, such as how to draw up graphs and describe patterns in results. Most pupils seemed able to draw a simple conclusion based on their evidence, for example:

> *'We found out that the biggest parachute came down slowest.'*

However, few pupils described patterns in results in detail, or attempted to interpret them. Often pupils were asked to write up the investigation on their own. Only a few teachers encouraged discussion amongst their pupils at this stage of the investigation. One example where there was discussion about the pattern and meaning of results was in a Y6 investigation into the the flow of current in a circuit. A group of more able pupils were given an ammeter to measure the current in a series circuit containing battery, bulb and a strip of pencil 'lead', i.e. graphite. As they altered the length of pencil 'lead' (resistance), they noted both the brightness of the bulb and, with some support, the reading on the ammeter. The measurements they took allowed them to draw up a line graph, discuss the pattern and work together to provide the following interesting commentary on their results.

> *'When you travel further down the lead, the difference (between readings) becomes less. The overall pattern in the graph is that the readings go down. If the pencil lead kept getting longer, the resistance would get greater and would*

eventually stop the flow of electricity. This would happen unless the volts of electricity (voltage) were greater.'

General Issues

There were some strategies that tended to be found in the more successful investigations. They were that teachers:

- identified clear aims for each investigation, knowing which skills and procedures they would highlight, and made their pupils aware of these aims
- allowed pupils to experience (play) with unfamiliar materials before focusing on planning
- taught skills and procedures explicitly to their pupils
- offered suitable support, sometimes in the form of prompt sheets, which they adapted to suit different types of investigations and different pupils
- offered support which allowed the pupils some, but not total, autonomy
- allowed time for working with the class or group to describe and interpret their results
- used formative assessment to develop skills.

Some of the difficulties encountered in investigations were caused by teachers and pupils not sharing the same meanings of the terms they were using. 'Fair Testing' was often used to mean more than the control of variables and was sometimes used in an everyday sense of fairness, which included making sure that measurements were taken accurately. Another example was the use of 'what you measure' as a user-friendly term for the dependent variable. These words were sometimes confusing for pupils, who assumed that 'what you measure' referred to anything to which they applied a ruler, thermometer, balance, measuring cylinder or stop-watch. In an investigation into the factors that affected the time a paper aeroplane stayed in the air, some pupils were asked to say what they were going to measure, i.e. to identify time in the air as the dependent variable. Instead they responded:

> *'We need to measure the length and width of the paper we use to make our plane. We need to weigh our plane to know how much blu-tack we have added.'*

In this instance, the teacher intervened successfully and clarified what was meant by 'what you measure'. There were other investigations where such interventions were not made and pupils remained confused.

Although teachers were aware of the importance of discussing technical terms related to science content with pupils, they rarely adopted the same strategy in connection with the language of investigations. Very few teachers spent time helping pupils to discriminate between words such as reliable, fair and accurate.

Also pupils did not usually recognise that they were learning skills and procedures, as well as knowledge, from investigative work. There was a mismatch between teachers' aims for investigations (over 50% of which were to teach procedures and skills) and the things pupils considered they had learnt during investigations (only 20% referred to procedures and skills, with half of these focusing on using equipment).

How Can We Improve Science Investigations in Schools?

The following suggestions may help to remedy some of the problems identified through the AKSIS Project.

- Draw pupils' attention to the different types of investigation and ensure that questions and prompts match the type of investigation undertaken.
- Identify which decisions will be taken by the teacher and which by the pupils. Do not expect pupils to take all planning decisions in every investigation.
- Teach pupils the skills and procedures of investigations, clarify how pupils can learn scientific procedures through doing an investigation and make them aware that this is the purpose of the lesson.
- Anticipate practical difficulties, particularly those related to measurement. Provide good equipment for pupils to use, appropriate to the degree of accuracy required by the task and the pupils' competence.
- Allow time to work with pupils to consider their evidence, using tables, bar charts and line graphs to explore patterns, make predictions and justify conclusions.
- Develop the language of investigations and teach pupils how to argue from evidence and challenge each other's results.
- Use formative assessment to stimulate pupils to make progress in the skills and procedures of investigation.

Summary

Although our primary science curriculum demands much of teachers and their pupils, it appears that pupils are making progress in their investigations. When asked how they thought pupils' performance in investigations had changed since the advent of the National Curriculum, the AKSIS teachers responded unanimously that it had improved. International comparisons also show that 13-year-old pupils from England and Singapore out-perform all other countries in this aspect of science (TIMSS 1998). If teachers can help pupils learn the scientific and language skills they need to investigate in different ways, we can expect further improvement. Our pupils may yet surprise us, and the rest of the world, with what they can achieve.

About the Author

Anne Goldsworthy is an experienced teacher in the primary sector. She is now an educational consultant and Chair of the ASE Primary Science Committee. She is the author of numerous publications on science education.

References and further reading

ASE (1998) *Policy Statements on Learning and Teaching, Quality in Science Education and Values and Science Education.* Hatfield, Herts, Association for Science Education.

DFE (1995) *Science in the National Curriculum*. HMSO.

Harris, S. with Keys, W. and Fernandes, C. (1997) *Third International Mathematics and Science Study, Third National Report*. Achievement in Mathematics and Science Practical Activities at Age 13 in England. Slough, NFER.

Goldsworthy, A. and Feasey, R. with Ball, S. (1997) *Making Sense of Primary Science Investigations*. ASE.

Goldsworthy, A. (1997) *Sometimes It's Not Fair. Primary Science Review,* No 53. ASE.

Watson, R. (1997) ASE–King's Science Investigations in Schools Project: Investigations at Key Stages 2 and 3 *Education in Science,* No 171, pp 22–23.

Watson, R., Goldsworthy, A. and Wood-Robinson, V.(1997) Getting AKSIS to Investigations *Education in Science,* No 177.

*The **A**SE and **K**ing's College **S**cience Investigations in **S**chools Project is a three-year research project focused on Key Stages 2 and 3, run jointly by the Association for Science Education and King's College, London and funded by the Wellcome Trust. It aims to explore the effects of Sc1 of the National Curriculum on current practice and to make recommendations for its future development, as well as helping teachers develop successful strategies for teaching science investigations.*

2.3 Scientific Investigations in Context

Rosemary Feasey

Investigations in primary science have become an established part of classroom activity. But classroom practice is an evolutionary process and part of that process is to ensure that the conventional rules and procedures of science investigations used by children do not remain static but are put to the test in dynamic and powerful contexts. This chapter explores the significance of such contexts in providing an audience to bridge the gap between children and their science and the wider world.

Scientific Investigation

Somebody goes somewhere and if there is a ghost they try to investigate it.
(Collette, aged 7)

Investigation is trying to find out about a thing.
(Simone, aged 8)

Young children, as the quotations suggest, can hold a range of ideas about what the word investigate means. Although Collette's definition might be more intriguing, Simone's is closer to the dictionary definition, which is 'to find out'. Investigations in science are about finding out, but finding out in a particularly rigorous way, one which attempts to mirror how scientists think and work.

However, it must be emphasised that not all practical activities in science are investigations, there are other kinds of practical activities which have been described by a number of different authors Gott and Duggan (1995), Feasey (1993) and Feasey (1997). These activities include observation, research, illustration, exploration, surveys, skills and handling secondary data. Practical activities should always be used by teachers on the basis of fitness for purpose.

What differentiates investigations from these other activities is the specific demands that they make on children to bring together skills such as using equipment, tables and graphs, knowledge of how to plan, carry out and evaluate fair tests and science concepts such as forces. Investigations, as Feasey (1997) has indicated, 'make a complex set of demands on children related to thinking and working scientifically'. Investigations demand that children are able to synthesize concepts, they demand knowledge of how and why to apply different skills, and they demand an awareness of the need to generate the sort of evidence that can be believed.

Much support has been offered to teachers on defining and teaching science investigations. The National Curriculum programmes of study offer a clear framework for investigations, whilst the work of Harlen (1994), Gott and Duggan (1995) and Feasey and Goldsworthy (1995) have explored key issues and offered support for teachers in the early stages of teaching National Curriculum investigations. (See Chapter 2.2).

Science Investigations in Social Contexts

The most important challenge for the future relates to the whole of the science curriculum and in particular, to science investigations. It is 'contextualisation'. Sometimes science in the primary curriculum can be in danger of becoming sterile and irrelevant to young children. There are fortunately, many more examples of investigations, across the key stages, taught in contexts familiar to the children. For example, children investigating movement using toy cars or friction using the shoes which children wear.

A child will usually be doing their work for the teacher, any concept of an audience for their work is vague. To be truly effective, we need to develop two crucial elements, firstly, widen the concept of audience and secondly make it one to whom children are responsible. (Feasey and Siraj-Blatchford, 1998)

The challenge of investigative work in science in the primary classroom is to develop the elements of 'audience' and 'responsibility'. These are found when investigations are developed in what Feasey and Siraj-Blatchford describe as a clear 'social context'. They argue that investigations set within a social context:

1. offer a purpose for carrying out an investigation
2. provide a specific audience for the children's investigation
3. demand that children consider the needs of the audience when planning, carrying out and evaluating an investigation
4. demand that the children have a responsibility to that audience to carry out an investigation which offers reliable and valid results
5. expect that children will communicate their investigation in an appropriate way to their audience.

The following social contexts are suggested by Feasey and Siraj-Blatchford (1998).

Industry – Children link with an industry which offers them a problem to solve, question to answer, or a particular project in which they have to carry out an investigation. Children could communicate with the industry using fax, e-mail, formal written report, letters.

Consumers – Children take on the role of a consumer action group, their audience might be parents or other children. A 'Which?' type report or a leaflet may be their final product that explains their activities and findings.

Environment – Issues raised about the local environment might be tackled in partnership with a local environmental agency, the audience could be the agency or the local community. Newspaper articles, leaflets, a web page are all appropriate methods of communicating to this type of audience.

Community – Issues might range from investigations into litter around the school, to 'saving energy'. There could be a range of audiences from parents to school governors or younger children. A newsletter, poster or formal presentation outlining their work and recommendations could be used to communicate in this case.

Themselves/peer group – Children sometimes investigate questions which relate directly to themselves, for example, the relationship between pulse rate and exercise. The audience could also be other children in their school or another 'partner' school with whom children could share, discuss and compare their investigations and results.

'Blue skies research' – Those rare occasions when children investigate something for the sake of doing it can be highly motivating. In these cases the audience is the children themselves and they are acting as a scientific community with a critical audience of their peers.

The Role of an Audience in Investigations

The use of social contexts offers an important dimension to investigative work. The concept of audience and responsibility to that audience is crucial and mirrors the work of scientists who are responsible to other scientists, the public and/or their 'paymasters'. A simple example is someone researching fitness and the effect of exercise on heart/pulse rate. The researchers have a responsibility to their audience, who, in this case may be athletes, to ensure that any advice offered is based on research which is valid and reliable. Incorrect advice could be life-threatening.

The social context provides the audience to which the children are responsible at *all* points throughout their investigation. Central to these investigations is the idea that the children will be expected to communicate their work to an audience and that the audience will be able to challenge what they are told. This is a much more accurate account of science as it is practised. Scientists work within different contexts and each of those contexts demand different communication skills. Sometimes scientists communicate with an external audience, but they also communicate within their own community. Similarly, children might communicate to people outside the school or to their own peer group.

In planning, carrying out and evaluating their investigation children have to:

- consider what their audience needs to know
- shape the investigation to ensure that they are working towards
- answering the question or problem set
- ensure that the investigation is carried out to collect valid and reliable data which can be believed
- consider whether they are able to answer the original question or problem using the data collected
- think about how to present information from the investigation in an appropriate manner to their audience.

There are a number of generic questions which apply across the different contexts that children will have to consider when communicating their investigation to a specific audience. For example:

- Who is the audience?
- What do they need to know?
- Which parts of the investigation are the most important?
- Are there certain parts of the investigation that can be left out?

- Can different parts of the investigation be explained in different ways, e.g. table, flow diagram, graph?
- Does the audience need any additional information and what extra research do we need to do?
- In what order should the information be presented?
- How can we show to the audience that they can be confident in our results?

Which way should we use to communicate the investigation to the audience? For example:

graphs	storyboards	leaflets
tables	letters	multimedia
prose	reports	shadow puppets
diagrams	photographs	slides
fax	video	OHP
e-mail	presentations	newspaper article
Internet		

The above questions and methods of communication constitute a writing 'frame'; not one imposed by the teacher but one which can be created by the children, sometimes in negotiation with the audience. However, communication must not be a one way process; offering investigations in a social context provides children with a potentially critical audience, one which should challenge the content of their communication by asking children to:

- explain aspects their investigation
- defend their approach
- consider results from another viewpoint
- be critical
- offer an analysis of their data rather than just a description of the investigation
- evaluate what they have done
- sometimes extend their investigation further.

Which is the Best Plastic Cup?

The following is an example of children working in a social context taken from the 'Key Skills In Science Project' at Durham. Year 6 children were given a problem by the catering company that supplied the school meals and a range of other functions. The company indicated in a letter to the children that they wanted to change the type of plastic cup they used for hot drinks after customers complained that the cups they were using were too hot to handle and did not keep the drinks hot for longer than a few minutes.

The children researched plastic cups and looked at 'Which?' type consumer reports. After carrying out a series of insulation investigations on different plastic cups, the children communicated their findings to their audience (the Catering Company) in the form of a consumer test report. Their report included details of how the investigations were carried out, a range of data, an analysis of the data and final recommendations, plus safety tips about using different cups.

In publishing their work, the children learned to use an adult computer package within a few hours and created page layouts which included text and graphs and scanned in art work. They reached a higher level of attainment than they had previously in their science work.

The catalyst for the rise in the standard of both their investigation and communication in science was clearly the social context and audience to whom the children were responsible. An important aspect of this work was the relationship between the children and the catering company. The children were investigating on behalf of someone else who was able to challenge their way of working and their findings. The power of the social context and influence of offering children an audience should not be underestimated.

Developing investigations in a social context moves science teaching and learning in the primary classroom from being two dimensional, that is between the teacher and child, to a multi-dimensional experience. Social contexts help to set the framework for investigative work and provide children with a real reason for doing science.

About the Author

Rosemary Feasey is a lecturer in primary science education at the School of Education, University of Durham. She is involved in research and curriculum development in science and an author of a range of science resources for primary teachers and children.

References and Further Reading

Department for Education (1995) *Science in the National Curriculum*. London, HMSO.

Feasey R. (1994) *The Challenge of Science*. In Aubrey C. *The Role of Subject Knowledge in the Early Years of Schooling*. London, Falmer Press.

Feasey R. (1997) *Thinking and Working Scientifically*. In Skamp, K. *Teaching Primary Science Constructively*. New South Wales, Harcourt Brace.

Feasey R. and Siraj-Blatchford J. (1998) *Key Skills in Science*. Durham University Tyneside Training and Enterprise Council Funded Project – work in progress.

Gott, R. and Duggan, S. (1995), *Developing Science and Technology Education Investigative Work in the Science Curriculum*. Buckingham, Open University Press.

Osborne J. (1991) Approaches to the Teaching of AT16 the Earth in Space: Issues, problems and resources. *School Science Review*, Vol 72, No 260, pp 7–15.

Phipps, R., Feasey, R., Gott., R. and Stringer, J. (1996) *Star Science Teachers' Resource Book*. Aylesbury, Ginn and Co. Ltd.

Rassan, C.C. (1193) *The Second Culture: British Science in Crisis – The Scientists Speak Out*. London, Aurum Press.

Sherrington, R. (Ed) (1993) *ASE Primary Science Teachers' Handbook*. Hempstead, UK, Simon and Schuster.

2.4 Learning Science in the Early Years

Jane Johnston

Early years' science experiences are the important first step to future scientific development. They can be formal or informal, pre-school or within compulsory education, at home or in an educational context. They are all-important. They are often experiential play activities or explorations which can develop affective and scientific attitudes, scientific skills and conceptual understandings. There are some important factors which affect the success of these early scientific experiences. The practical nature of experiences, the context of the experiences, the quality and quantity of adult interaction, the opportunities to develop linguistic skills and the focusing of attention on learning objectives, are some of the most important. In education we need to value the place of early years science as a foundation for future scientific development and to nurture the partnership between home and school to facilitate future success in science education.

The State of Early Years' Education

During the late 1990s popular and political interest in early years' education has resulted in some focusing on what is good practice and how the education of young children can be better served. *The recognition of desirable outcomes* (SCAA, 1996) for early years' education is felt to provide a foundation for scientific learning. These outcomes include young children's understanding of the world, with particular emphasis on *the environment, other people and features of the natural and made world* (SCAA, 19964). The recognition of learning outcomes for children entering compulsory education, together with three other elements:

- coherent planning
- a true partnership with parents and carers (SCAA, 1997a; DfEE.1997) and
- baseline assessment (SCAA, 1997b)

should go a long way to improve pre-school education as a whole, as well as, more specifically, science education.

The introduction of science as a core subject in the curriculum for children aged five and above has had a significant effect on children's skills and conceptual understandings. Since pre-school experiences are the foundation for future interests, skills and understandings, I hope that improvement in early years' provision in science education will become compulsory in the future. Good practice in early years' science has been publicised through exemplars (SCAA, 1997a). We might hope that such exemplars will focus on what is good in science education and discourage the trend to teach science as a separate subject, and divorced from reality. This trend has become common at Key Stage 2 and is increasingly and alarmingly seen more often at Key Stage 1. (See also Chapters 2.6 and 2.7.)

What is Good Practice in Early Years' Education?

The beginnings of scientific development occur at birth, or even before, as we experience the world around us. As babies and young children we observe events, use our senses to explore the world around us and develop theories to explain what we observe. Bath and meal times, being taken out in the pram or push chair and listening to the noises around, all contribute to our understandings. For example, we learn at an early age about gravity as we drop things out of our prams or high chairs (Johnston, 1996a:S) and 'it becomes a game to throw away your toys and wait for someone else to rescue them'. Young children who play this look down for the toys they drop. This is the beginning of understanding about forces which will develop throughout the child's life.

Some educationalists and more particularly, some scientists believe that informal experiences are unlikely to have a significant effect on scientific development, particularly conceptual development. This may be, in part, because many formal experiences are seen to lead to scientific misconceptions. Additionally, it is thought that you cannot be said to have scientific skills or understandings if you use them without full knowledge of what you are doing. Take for example, a young child who knows from the experience of growing plants in the garden that they grow faster in the summer when the sun is shining and the leaves are green. The child may apply that knowledge to gardening without really knowing about the processes of growth or any understanding of photosynthesis. Could we say that the child has no real scientific knowledge? I prefer to think that the child is using informal science knowledge and is developing understanding about the world through informal experiences which will be built upon in more formal learning situations.

I have previously described scientific development (Johnston, 1996a:27) as a double helix where knowledge and understanding develop alongside skills through experience. A more refined model is a triple helix where the three strands of development – scientific conceptual understanding, skills and attitudes – develop together in an inter-linked spiral, with experiences being the important linking strands (see Fig 2.4A).

Practical Experiences

The kind of early experiences which move children up the learning spiral in the three areas are memorable, practical ones. For example, children who are allowed to help make pastry and play with some left-over dough may observe the differences between the flour before and after mixing with water, experience the feel of the flour and pastry and have an enjoyable learning experience. They will be motivated and encouraged, wanting to see the finished results of any baked pastry shapes, making them want to learn. They may begin to develop useful future scientific and generic attitudes, such as co-operation with their siblings or friends and respect for the ideas of others. They will develop useful scientific skills, such as observation and the ability to hypothesize as to why things happen. They will also develop scientific

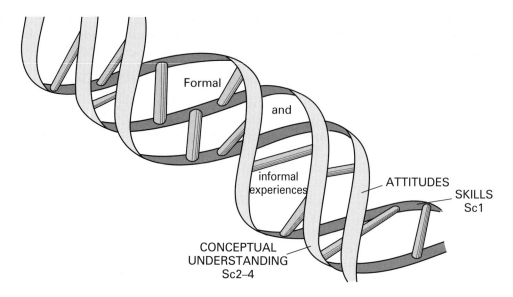

Formal

and

informal experiences

ATTITUDES

SKILLS
Sc1

CONCEPTUAL
UNDERSTANDING
Sc2–4

Fig 2.4A The development of scientific conceptual understanding, skills and attitudes

conceptual understandings about the properties of the materials they are using and how they change when mixed and heated. These experiences are important in future development because a child who is not motivated, does not know how to co-operate and has no theories as to what will happen to everyday materials when mixed with water or heated, will thereby be disadvantaged in their formal education by their lack of pre-school experiences.

The move from informal, pre-school experiences to formal ones should not be a giant step for children, but a continuation which will enhance development within the three areas of learning. These experiences will continue to be practical and motivating but they will also be a more focused look at the everyday familiar world of the child. The teacher's role is to build upon previous development and to provide practical, motivating activities which have specific learning objectives. These three aspects of teaching and learning in the early years are inextricably linked; good learning will only occur if all three are in place.

Ice Balloons

My recent interactions with 4- and 5-year-old children in their first term of formal schooling involved exploring ice balloons (water filled balloons which are then frozen). Whilst well-tried and tested (Johnston, 1996) ice balloons never cease to motivate and develop useful skills such as observation and the ability to raise questions. My learning objectives were to develop motivational attitudes, observational skills and conceptual understanding about materials and their properties. The resources used, together with the interaction between the children and myself and particularly the questions asked, aided the achievement of these objectives.

I began by giving the children an ice balloon well wrapped up in newspaper and asking them to tell me what they noticed about it. They passed it around and immediately began to use their senses to make observations of the package, such as, *'It's cold'*, *'It's heavy'*, *'It's making a cracking noise inside'* and to use their previous experiences, *'It feels like a frozen chicken'*. Later observations of the unwrapped balloon led one child to comment that I had frozen the air inside the balloon. We then focused on the properties of three different balloons, one filled with air, one with water and one ice balloon. The children began to compare the properties of the different balloons, *'This one is squashy'*, *'Both water and air are squashy'*, *'This one is harder than the others'*.

They then began to predict what would happen if they dropped the balloons; *'It will bounce'*, *'This one will smash'*, *'I think it will break'*. We then decided to observe what did happen if we dropped the balloons from a height and the children became very interested in their observations of the water-filled balloon which broke on impact and made some very interesting patterns on the dry pavement in the school playground.

Through this motivating, practical experience, the children not only had opportunities to use their previous knowledge and skills, but they also developed their observational skills and understanding about the nature of air, water and ice. They developed their language skills and vocabulary by describing their observations and discussing with others. They also began to realise that other children hold different ideas from their own, an important step to tolerating and accepting others' ideas.

Fig 2.4B 'This one is squashy' (Children at St. Mary's C of E Primary School, Sutton-in Ashfield)

Explorations and Play

These experiences are often forms of play (Moyles, 1994), and recognised as essential to children's early development (Bennett, Wood and Rogers, 1997), but are not always a feature of classroom practice. I have referred to such experiences as explorations (Johnston, 1996). For the early years child, exploration, whether structured or unstructured can be a learning experience in itself, developing attitudes, skills and conceptual understandings. For older children, exploration is an essential prerequisite to further investigation. This is because we all need a period of unstructured play or exploration to focus our ideas. Exploration has an important part to play in the scientific process. Dale-Tunnicliffe and Reiss (1997) found that, when observing brine shrimps, children developed understandings about the processes of life. Combined with observations of other mini-beasts (such as worms, woodlice and snails), the variety of life and similarities and differences between living things can be understood. These explorations should be very practical in nature, as experiential learning is more likely to develop understandings.

The Role of Parents

The continued support of parents in pre-school and early school education cannot be stressed too strongly. We can involve parents more effectively in the scientific development of their children in a number of ways. General help in the classroom can be of great assistance when children are engaged in a scientific exploration. In most early explorations, children benefit from a clear focus and questions which will help to develop the learning objectives for the activity. A classroom helper or parent can easily ask these questions and assist in the children's learning. Some parents have special expertise which would assist in developing understanding. For example, a parent who is a baker can give children an insight into the baking process and an optician could provide glasses for the children to play with and show the children how the glasses change what we see.

Parents can also aid children's scientific development through experiences at home. They may provide a range of differing experiences for their children. These may include focusing attention on events, such as how a snail moves across the garden or how the bubbles rise to the top of a fizzy drink, or, more generally, allowing them longer to play in the bath with some floating and sinking toys, playing with soap bubbles made with washing up liquid or helping with the baking. Most importantly, parents can be good role models by learning with the children, questioning, making observations and hypothesising as to why something is happening.

Context

The context of early experiences is another important factor affecting development. Contexts need to be familiar, as this supports the early learner and helps them to see the relevance of science to everyday life. For example, if developing ideas about friction it is better to ask children to explore which of their shoes have the best grip or if developing ideas about insulation to ask which clothes would be better for teddy to wear in the winter. The contextualization can also help children to use science in decision-making in later life and in being good citizens.

Classroom Interaction

Possibly the most important factor affecting development will be the type of inter-action with adults during science experiences. All adults need to be good role models, showing children that learning is fun, adopting a questioning, interested approach, being tentative in their ideas and valuing the ideas the children and other adults hold. I find that in most interactions with children, I learn as much as they do and benefit from an insight into their thinking and enthusiasm.

In a recent observation in a class of 5-year-old children, a student teacher had the whole class together to develop understanding about forces. She was using some toys, but the children were not handling them themselves and were losing attention fast. She was finding it very difficult and becoming flustered.

In another situation, children were successfully developing understanding about forces through exploration of artefacts from around the home. These included nutcrackers, scissors, garlic press, bottle opener, cork screw, screwdriver, hole punch and salad spinner. The children were asked to explore the objects and to see how they worked. During their explorations either the teacher or the nursery nurse in the class asked the children some open-ended, personalised questions, such as: 'How do you think these work?' 'What do you notice about.....?' 'What will happen if ....?' The adults also expressed a personal interest in the objects and made their own observations and articulated their own questions. After the exploration, the children described their observations to the whole class and explained their hypotheses as to how and why the objects worked. The teacher was encouraging their language development as well as their scientific understanding of forces around the home through the opportunities provided and the questioning approach. As importantly, the teacher showed interest and motivation, wanting to learn from the experience herself.

Early childhood development is a fascinating and exciting area of education to be involved in. As teachers, we have as much to learn from our experiences with children as they have from the experiences we provide for them. It is imperative that we make these early scientific experiences positive learning experiences. It will also help them to develop into well-rounded individuals, excited and curious about the world around them, not afraid to question their ideas and the ideas of others and who can see the value of scientific skills and conceptual understandings in their everyday lives.

About the Author

Jane Johnston is a senior lecturer in primary education at Bishop Grosseteste University College, where she specialises in early years' and primary science education. Her particular interests are in early years' science education and the development of attitudes to science.

References and further reading

Bastiani, J. (1996) Home–School liaison: the Mainstreaming of Good Ideas and Effective Practice. In Bastiani, J. and Wolfendale, S. (1996) *Home–School Work in Britain: Review, Reflection and Development.* London, David Fulton.

Bennett, N., Wood, L. and Rogers, S. (1997) *Teaching Through Play: Teachers' Thinking and Classroom Practice.* Buckingham, OUP.

CACE (Central Advisory Council for Education) (1967) *Children and their Primary Schools.* London, HMSO.

Dale Tunnicliffe, S. and Reiss, M. (1997) *Conversations in Science: What Children bring to Brine Shrimps.* Paper presented to the European Science Educational Research Association 1997.

DfEE (1997) *Early Years Development Partnerships and Plans.*

Johnston, J. (1996a) *Early Exploration in Science.* Buckingham, Open University Press.

Johnston, J. (1996b) *Parents Facilitating Educational Development in the Primary Child: Current Practice and Future Development.* Paper presented to the British Educational Research Association 1996.

Moyles, J. (Ed) (1994) *The Excellence of Play.* Buckingham, Open University Press.

SCAA (School Curriculum and Assessment Authority) (1996) *Nursery Education: Desirable Outcomes for Children's Learning on Entering Compulsory Education.* DfEE/SCAA.

SCAA (1997a) *Looking at Children's Learning: Desirable Outcomes for Children's Learning on Entering Compulsory Education.* London, SCAA.

SCAA (1997a) *The National Framework for Baseline Assessment: Criteria and procedures for the accreditation of baseline assessment schemes.* London, SCAA.

Acknowledgement

Thank you to the staff and children of St. Mary's C.of E. Primary School in Sutton-in-Ashfield, Nottinghamshire for their help.

2.5 Opinions and Values in Learning Science

Mary Ratcliffe and Roger Lock

We consider that learning about the social and ethical applications of science is a key element of pupils' entitlement in science education. In this chapter we examine some of the barriers to consideration of values, opinions and arguments in science lessons and provide practical guidance to assist teaching and learning.

Introduction

The class have just had Assembly, where the head teacher has been praising pupils for their good behaviour but expressing concern over the lack of support for the recycling project. She urges pupils to bring clean waste paper to the recycling point and not throw it in bins or, worse, on the ground. The class enters the room where the teacher is ready to start a lesson on materials. A pupil spies the different materials and says, 'Miss, I think this recycling paper business is stupid, don't you? Doesn't it take energy and money to recycle things?' Before the teacher can reply, another pupil pipes in, 'Don't be silly, the school can get money from scrap paper. They want us to do the cleaners' work.' Faced with an involved discussion, the teacher urges pupils to their seats and starts the lesson in the way planned. She asks pupils to think about ways of sorting the everyday materials. She expects pupils to develop a sorting system which reflects some of the physical properties of the materials.

Why did the teacher not use the opportunity presented by the pupils' comments to start the lesson with a discussion about recycling paper?

We suspect that opportunities like this may not be taken up because of:

1 perceived dominance of acquiring knowledge of abstract facts and concepts, encouraged by the assessment system.
2 lack of confidence or ability in handling discussions where there may be no 'correct' answers but a range of value judgements.
3 lack of clear teaching strategies to cope with controversial, social issues.
4 views that social applications of science should not be part of the science curriculum.

It is helpful to define terms and trace the history of this aspect of the curriculum before considering appropriate teaching strategies.

What Do We Mean by Social and Ethical Applications of Science?

Social applications of science are those which impinge on our lives everyday directly and indirectly through political and economic decision making. Science provides us with the evidence for what we can do, whether it be cloning, 'splitting' the atom or making new chemicals. Science is a process of rational enquiry which seeks to propose explanations for observations of natural phenomena. Ethics helps us to decide what we should do. Ethics is a process of rational enquiry by which we decide on issues of right (good) and wrong (bad) as applied to people and their actions (Fullick and Ratcliffe, 1996).

Development of Social and Ethical Issues in Science Curricula in England and Wales

Up to the early 1980s it was unusual for social and ethical issues to be considered in science lessons; only the occasional, committed enthusiast introduced such applications. ASE produced a consultative document (ASE, 1979) which, amongst other proposals, mooted a social context for science work. This document influenced the nature of the new GCSE syllabuses that were developed in 1983.

A further bid for status for social and ethical issues in science was made in one of the early drafts of a Science National Curriculum. In the proposed attainment target 21, Science in Action, it was suggested that:

> *Pupils should develop a critical awareness of the ways that science is applied in their own lives and in industry and society, of its personal, social and economic implications, benefits and drawbacks.*

By proposing to devote a complete attainment target to such issues a clear signal could be given to pupils and teachers about the status of such work. However, by the time a statutory version of the curriculum had been produced the attainment target been deleted. References to ethical issues were limited.

Not only were the social, moral and ethical issues marginalised in terms of their status within the curriculum, but they were often included in a position which suggested that study of such issues was only appropriate for older and most able pupils.

In the revised 1995 National Curriculum social and ethical considerations were in the preamble to the detail of the programmes of study. This section, which applies across all science teaching, makes clear, in Key Stages 1 and 2, that pupils should be given opportunities such as the study of the impact of science on everyday life and consideration of living things and the environment. By Key Stage 4 it is made explicit that pupils should 'consider the power and limitations of science in addressing industrial, social and environmental issues and some of the ethical dilemmas involved'.

This version of the Science National Curriculum leaves it open for teachers to decide in which contexts the social and ethical applications are considered, whereas in the version of the curriculum that it replaced, the statements of attainment identified specific contexts. It would seem that the study of social and ethical issues continues to be marginalised.

Why Should Social and Ethical Issues Be Addressed in Science Lessons?

For most people the period of formal, compulsory education is the major lifetime opportunity for understanding the science that will impact on their lives and lifestyles. As adults we are expected to play a full and responsible role in society which includes applying the knowledge, understanding and the attitudes and opinions, gained from our study of school science, to our everyday life. However, there are some who consider that social and ethical issues should only be considered in Religious Education or in teaching about Personal, Social and Health Education. Such views are even shared by some teachers of science. The view we develop here is that those teaching science have a special and unique contribution to make to learning about social and ethical issues. We do not, however, deny the right of other subjects to involve lessons on such topics. Indeed we think it can only be good for the profile of science that it is included in cross-curricular contexts, as it is in this way that the distinctive contributions that science and scientists make become evident.

Chapter 1.1 outlines the overlapping reasons for learning science. These should not be treated discretely. By exploring the social and ethical applications of science pupils may also acquire knowledge and will come to understand the methods of science.

The important first step is to include the learning about social and ethical science issues in work schemes as an integral part of science study. They should not be seen as an 'add on' at the end of a topic, as an extra for homework nor as the final element of material for fast workers, but as a central theme covered by all pupils. In this way the marginalisation, discussed in the previous section, will be avoided.

Having included such work, the unique contribution from science becomes evident. We are the ones who have the conceptual knowledge that underpins the controversial issues involved be they using animals to test medicines, producing electricity or eating beefburgers. We have access to the data and information that informs such issues and the opportunity to see them in the broader science context. Our closeness to the knowledge base and the inevitable interaction of pupils with this in their learning, shows how lessons about social and ethical applications of science will also contribute to pupils' science knowledge.

Our training should also ensure that we bring a 'scientific approach' to lessons involving such work. As teachers of science we can help pupils to distinguish between fact and opinion. We can encourage them to question the limits of accuracy of presented data and to check whether the interpretation offered is supported by the data. Such strategies help pupils to develop a respect for evidence and encourage the kind of open-mindedness to which scientists aspire. Working in such way can develop a tolerance to uncertainty and an appreciation of the probability limits within which particular interpretations apply.

We have an important role in helping pupils to understand an argument and to try to judge the validity of the 'expert' scientists' work. We should also be encouraging pupils to make up their own minds and to develop their own opinions and attitudes. We should try to ensure that such opinions are soundly based, that pupils are able to distinguish between fact and hearsay as well as able to critically evaluate the evidence. The exact nature of the pupil opinion should not be important, but gaining it through critical reflection and respect for evidence is.

We have shown how learning about social and ethical applications of science means that pupils don't just learn science and science practical skills, they also learn about the ways in which scientists work and think. Through this latter perspective pupils will come to see scientists in a different light. No longer the cold, hard, uncaring, unsympathetic and eccentric, balding male, but the warm considerate person concerned about the ethical dilemmas that her work produces. Pupils might come to see that scientists are not the 'boffins' that cause society's ills and problems, but the agents who are trying to alleviate them. Such a view is firmly aligned with current concerns about the wider accountability of scientists and ways in which they and their work is perceived by the general public. One central pillar of this concern about pupils' understanding of science is to come to appreciate that the moral high ground is not the exclusive preserve of non-scientists.

Values in Science Education

Social and ethical applications of science require consideration of attitudes and values, which seem difficult areas for science teachers to engage in. Yet, in every science class in the country values are being transmitted.

Values are inherent in science. The ASE policy on values and science education considers that values which guide scientists' conduct include expectations:

- to be thorough in all operations, including observation, calculation and reporting
- to be intellectually honest, e.g. refraining from exaggeration, not plagiarising
- to be open-minded, e.g. willing to look for and consider new evidence, facts and theories
- to suspend judgement rather than make snap judgements
- to be self-critical and to encourage others to criticise one's work.

These values of science can be mirrored in consideration of the social and ethical of science.

Planning for Teaching and Learning

The 'content' for social and ethical applications of science is readily available. Local and topical issues, applications of science relevant to the science topic are all appropriate. This section outlines useful methods for handling social and ethical issues.

In all these methods, particular views and values will be shown. It is important to be clear of the purpose of the activity. Bridges (1979) argues that there may be a number of functions for discussion of a controversial issue:

a) sharing individual perspectives – a sufficient goal in itself
b) reaching an understanding of the variety of available subjective responses
c) making a choice between differing values
d) finding a rational resolution of the controversy.

This list implies a hierarchy of purposes – rational resolution being perhaps the most difficult to attain. In primary schools a) and b) seem the most realistic purposes.

For the chosen examples it may appear that people would not in practice give much, if any, consideration to scientific evidence in reaching an opinion. However, the intention in a science lesson is to show how scientific ideas and concepts interact with values and ideas from other disciplines.

We emphasise again that we see the goal of such activities as understanding the complexity and evidence base for viewpoints not the opinion arrived at itself.

1) Exploring What If? Questions – Consequence Mapping

Consequence mapping is a simple technique that can be used with pupils of a wide age range. It consists of posing 'What If?' questions and following through the consequences. It helps to consider two opposing 'What If?' questions to get a balanced picture of what might happen. Fig 2.5A shows a simple consequence map.

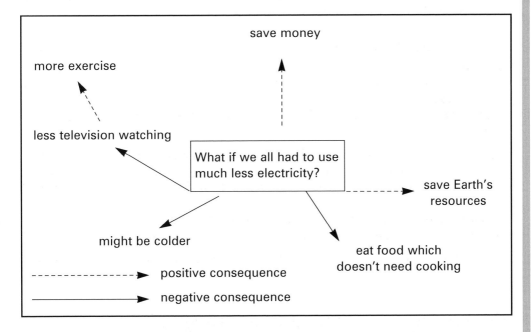

Fig 2.5A Simple consequence map

Examples of issues for consequence mapping:

- What if we all became vegetarians?
- What if pork was the only type of meat available? (This brings in a cultural and religious dimension.)

2) Focused Questions/Structured Debate

An easy way to introduce topical issues is to encourage debate around a focused question. This is used in many resources and, if the question is posed appropriately, prompts much discussion. However, it is easy for discussions to become a sharing of views without clear evaluation of the arguments and evidence. Without a structure those most willing to express their views are heard, without all having an opportunity to debate the issue.

Strategies for allowing most pupils to become engaged with the issue include:

- Turn-taking – only the person holding the 'discussion stone' can speak.
- 'Snowball' discussions – twos, then fours then eights, with a limited number of points for each group to make.

The teacher has to decide what role to adopt during the debate, particular if pupils' views clash with informed views of an adult. The teacher may disclose their own views explaining the reasons, act as a neutral chair or play devil's advocate. (Ratcliffe, 1998.)

Examples of focused questions:

Should animals be kept in school?
Should we save waste paper for recycling?

3) Role Play

A strategy which is useful for some issues is to act out the positions of the people involved. It allows pupils to empathise more closely with situations which they may come across later. It can be motivating for many pupils to engage with an issue in this way. However, role play has a number of pitfalls which can prevent good analysis of an issue. The purpose and 'science' in an issue can easily get lost as pupils get into role – the personal characteristics becoming more important than evidence. This allows pupils to see the feelings and values involved but can also affect their own views. This is particularly true if they have been put in an emotional position without considering their own reaction. Whenever role play is used for controversial and emotionally charged issues, de-briefing of roles at the end is important. Pupils need to talk through their feelings of being in role and their own views.

Example of issue for role play: Should all children be vaccinated against flu? (Roles: doctor, parent, children with different views towards vaccination.)

4) Goals, Rights and Duties

A particular strategy useful for ethical dilemmas as well as more general social issues is that of 'Goals, Rights and Duties' (Fullick and Ratcliffe, 1996). For each person or group of people affected by an issue, the goals, rights and duties are considered:

Goal – What the person intends to accomplish through a particular action.
Right – Entitlement to particular kind of treatment no matter what the consequences.
Duty – Obligation to act or behave in a particular way.
Goals, rights and duties may be dependent on the culture and religion of the locality. Pupils are likely to find some conflict arises when considering the different people involved. This activity is not a way of providing a neat answer to a difficult issue but of showing the complexity of the issue. It allows pupils to see how different viewpoints on an issue may be justifiably reached.

Fig 2.5B shows an example of how pupils might consider the goals, rights and duties of people involved in cigarette manufacture. This can be added to by considering other people involved such as Government, tobacco company employees, tobacco growers, etc.

Person	Goals	Rights	Duties
Manager of cigarette company	Make profit	Sell cigarettes Advertise cigarettes?	Treat employees fairly Provide safe products
Non-smoker	Healthy and enjoyable life	Healthy environment Spend money as wishes	Fairness to others
Smoker	Enjoyable and healthy life	Spend money as wishes Enjoy habit	Fairness to others

Fig 2.5B Goals, rights and duties in cigarette manufacture

Example of issue for goals, rights and duties: Should pigs/mice/apes be used in medical research?

With all these methods there are advantages and disadvantages. We encourage use of a variety. Those with an analytical framework, however, may be more helpful in relating social issues to the analytical nature of science. They may also assist in developing analytical skills useful in consideration of scientific issues as well as social issues.

About the Authors

Mary Ratcliffe has taught chemistry and science in comprehensives in Suffolk and Essex, including periods as head of department. She is currently a senior lecturer in education at the University of Southampton with research interests in pupils' learning science in a social context.

Roger Lock is a native of Norfolk and a graduate of Aberdeen University. He taught in Kilmarnock, Birmingham and Leamington Spa. He has worked in the Universities of Leeds and Oxford and is currently senior lecturer in education at the University of Birmingham.

References and Further Reading

ASE (1979) *Alternatives for Science Education: a consultative document.* Hatfield, ASE.

ASE (1997) *Values and Science Education: Policy Statement*. Hatfield, ASE.

Bridges, D. (1979) *Education, Democracy and Discussion*. Windsor, NFER Publishing Company.

Fullick, P. L. and Ratcliffe, M (1996) *Teaching Ethical Aspects of Science*. Totton, Bassett Press.

Ratcliffe, M. (1998) Discussing socio-scientific issues in science lessons – pupils' actions and the teacher's role. *School Science Review* Vol 79, No 288, pp 55–59.

Useful resources for providing examples of contexts:

ASE (1992) *SATIS 8–14* (Science and Technology in Society). Hatfield, ASE. Suitable for all UK curricula:

ASE (1996) *Science and Technology Ideas for the under 8's*. Hatfield, ASE.

ASE (1997) *SATIS Science Resources for KS2*. Hatfield, ASE. Five booklets: Health, Environment, Technology, Materials, Transport.

2.6 Environmental Education

John Stringer

Environmental education – education about, for and in the environment – is both relevant and significant in children's understanding of the world around them. Science has a special contribution in skills, knowledge and attitudes to the coherence of this area.

Why Teach about the Environment?

'Environment' has become a buzzword; a word so loaded with content, attitudes and opinions that is hard to define precisely what environmental education is all about. In 1988 that the Council and Ministers of Education of the Council of the European Community resolved that, as a matter of priority, environmental education should be promoted within all sectors of education within the community.

> *The objective of environmental education is to increase public awareness of the problems in this field, as well as provide possible solutions, and to lay the foundations for a fully informed and active participation of the individual in the protection of the environment and the prudent and rational use of natural resources.*

The Resolution provides the following guiding principles for environmental education:

> *– the environment as the common heritage of mankind;*
>
> *– the common duty of maintaining, protecting and improving the quality of the environment, as a contribution to the protection of human health and the safeguarding of the ecological balance;*
>
> *– the need for a prudent and rational utilisation of resources;*
>
> *– the way in which each individual can, by his own behaviour, particularly as a consumer, contribute to the protection of the environment.*

Challenging Children's Ideas

Children of all ages are aware of the need for an environmentally friendly way of life. Because environmental groups of many kinds have seized the moral high ground, children may have a simplistic approach – no progress is seen as good, while every industrial or commercial initiative is seen as bad. Wildlife gardens are good; building developments are bad. Bicycles are good; cars are bad.

Environmental education can be see as being about, for and in the environment. These three strands are intertwined.

Education about the Environment

The primary science curriculum has a clear role in educating children about the environment. Statements at both primary key stages in each of the curricula of the United Kingdom give teachers direction to teach children about their environment. Primary science is now less concerned with 'Nature Study' and more with the way that plants and animals 'manage', how they are adapted to their habitats and to changing conditions.

Education for the Environment

Once we understand these relationships, we also recognise their fragility, and the vulnerability of many habitats. Children need to recognise that alongside continuous natural changes, the effects of human intervention have made a significant impact – not all of it harmful – on the environment.

Education for the environment has to find ways to ensure children's caring use of the environment, and solutions to environmental problems, taking into account conflicting interests and a range of cultural perspectives. Education for the environment should be concerned with issues of quality, sustainability and interaction with the environment. Finally, it should enable children to feel confident in taking personal and public action to attain environmentally-friendly ends. Science education can offer opportunities for all of these.

Education in the Environment

Environmental education will have little relevance without first-hand experience outdoors. Primary schools have commonly seen this progressing from early experience of the immediate surroundings, later experiences beyond the home and school, local trips and visits and then visits further afield. With each experience, learning is through personal experiences and response. The scientific aspects of fieldwork can play a major role, and the geographical and historical aspects of a visit are also important; together they enrich the experience and develop environmental understanding.

In this way, pupils have regular first-hand experience of a range of nearby localities – the school grounds, the park, a nature garden – and increasing numbers of visits to places further afield – woodland, a pond, the seashore. In addition, good secondary sources can inform them about more distant environments and possibly prepare them for future visits. Learning can be greatly enriched by the wide range of excellent wildlife programmes on television.

The Curriculum Place of Environmental Education

Environmental education has an important curricular role to play in many curriculum subjects. In addition, the curriculum guidance of the NCC in 1990 states that knowledge about the environment is wide-ranging, and the skills of environmental education could cover communication, numeracy, study skills of all sorts, problem-solving, personal and social, and skills within information technology. The promotion of positive attitudes to the environment is essential if pupils are to understand that they have a role in safeguarding the future. Among the attitudes to develop are:

- appreciation of the environment, and care for living things
- the development of independent thought on environmental issues
- respect for the beliefs and opinions of others
- respect for evidence and rational argument
- tolerance and open-mindedness.

The Special Contribution of Science

Several disciplines are concerned with the use of evidence – among them, history and geography. Science is concerned with the importance of scientific evidence – evidence based upon rigorous investigation and fair testing – and with its evaluation, as a proof of argument. Thus pupils can learn to reject poorly-substantiated arguments and be critical of unconvincing or poorly-assembled evidence. Environmental education – where emotion can be involved to the point where heart rules head – has to be subject to the same rational thought that underlines all the other areas of science.

Science is also concerned with the evaluation and understanding of risk. Generally, we are poor at assessing risk. For example, lifts have an extraordinary safety record, yet few people would choose them as the safest form of transport. Recently, bitter arguments raged about the environmental risks involved in either sinking a disused oil rig or towing it to a fjord to be dismantled. While the latter seemed more environmentally friendly, the risks of spillage and environmental damage were far greater. In the event, the towing option was a success in spite of the risks.

Care and concern for living things and the environment underpins the science interests of many of those directly responsible for decisions affecting the environment. Fishing protection officers, forestry commissioners and country rangers will all, commonly, come from a science background. Many of them will be far more balanced about human impact than many apparently environmentally-friendly individuals and organisations. They are knowledgeable, realistic and enthusiastic.

Current Developments in Environmental Education

Increasing numbers of primary schools, have a policy concerned with waste disposal and recycling, water usage and the economical use of heating fuel and other resources. These can have significant effects on reducing wastage of natural resources through the reduction of school heating and resource use and consequent financial savings. In addition, the involvement of the whole school community in such an initiative is both educational and advantageous.

There are many support organisations for school grounds improvements. They assist schools with their plans plans for environmental areas, trees and plants for planting. Thousands of schools have had their grounds improved by enthusiastic teams of volunteers – an initiative which engages the school community in a coherent approach to environmental education.

The Woodland – an Example of Coherent Environmental Planning

Environmental education is concerned with the impact of people on the environment – and not all of that impact is negative.

A large primary school on the outskirts of a Midlands city had an area of woodland that was causing some concern. It had become overgrown and dangerous, and was thought to be a source of vermin. On its edge was a temporary building used by the local community, including a lively youth club. The members found the impenetrable woodland attractive for smoking, illegal drinking, and some wild activities. The school was suffering with complaints from neighbours and occasional vandalism.

The new head teacher had a great enthusiasm for environmental education, and saw the woodland as an opportunity. She approached the County Natural History Trust for advice and practical support in managing the woodland. She asked the youth club for help in clearing the undergrowth and opening up the wood. Over the next year, the ground was cleared, paths were cut, and a bridge built over a small stream. Bird and bat boxes were installed, and markers placed for children and others following a nature trail. Neighbours were enrolled to keep an eye on the improved woodland, and the youth club was given the freedom of the area – as wardens, rather than vandals.

Habitats of different kinds have been developed in the woodland. One area was left untouched as overgrown bramble, another was flooded and became marshland. Children regularly investigate the effect of shading or covering areas of the ground – and record the changes to the plants and animals.

That is not the end of the story, it is the beginning. The woodland is both controlled and remains 'natural'. Plants are encouraged and animals protected. Recently the owl box became inhabited and there are frogs in the slow-moving stream. A number of unusual birds has been spotted. There is evidence that a fox has taken up residence – a mile from a ring road. The annual management programme continues.

About the Author

John Stringer is a writer and INSET trainer in primary science and technology. He is an author of Star Science and Ginn Science, and directed the ASE SATIS 8–14 project.

References and Further Reading

ASE (1998) *Policy on Environmental Education.* The Association for Science Education.

NCC (1990) *The National Curriculum Council Curriculum Guidance 7: Environmental Education.*

ASE (1996) *Investigating the Environment at Key Stages 1 and 2.* The Association for Science Education/Nuclear Electric.

2.7 Science and Design and Technology

John Stringer

Design and technology and science are separate subjects with unique characteristics, but inextricable linkages. Design and technology will establish itself fully in the primary curriculum when its special contribution to the whole education of the child is recognised.

Design and Technology

In the early stages of National Curriculum development, attempts were made to link science and technology in one document. In practice, however, it proved difficult to reconcile the two because each has its own distinct processes and procedures and the two subjects were separate in the 1989 National Curriculum. The 1992 version of the National Curriculum incorporated design and information technology into the subject of design and technology. In 1995, information technology itself became a separate subject. Even now, in some primary schools, design and technology struggles to establish its unique position and lacks a clear identity on the curriculum.

Lewis Wolpert, (1997) Chairman of the Committee on the Public Understanding of Science in 1997–8, clarifies the differences between science and technology. Technology, he argues, has led to developments of real use and purpose and science is concerned with understanding the way the world works. No science, he says, was necessary to invent the bicycle, it is just a matter of 'fiddling with the wheels'. On the other hand, when Archimedes first explored how to balance two unequal weights on a level – by putting the heavier weight nearer the fulcrum – and discovered the mathematical relationships involved, he had made a great discovery of no practical advantage, but which led to scientific understanding . This, he says, was the beginning of physics, 'which provides the best model for science'.

When we are doing science, we are exploring the outside world and seeking to understand it. When doing technology, on the other hand, we are imagining and creating something which does not exist until we have made it. Science draws the world into our minds, technology makes changes to the world because of what we have envisaged.

Design and Technology in Schools

In primary education, a model of technology that is concerned with planning with a purpose, which follows a cycle informed by information, has developed. It can be illustrated in this way:

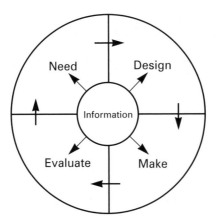

Fig 2.7A (Adapted from Goodhew, Lewin and Stringer (1991) Ginn Technology)

'Design and Make' has a long-established position in primary schools. To this is added the concept of designing to a purpose and of evaluation of products. Thus, activities as diverse as designing a new breakfast cereal and creating a new piece of playground apparatus both find their place in technology. Children evaluate the current range of breakfast cereals before mixing their own products or testing the strength and durability of their new playground slide – at least in model form – after constructing it. Both these stages and the design and make process are informed by children's understanding of the dietary needs of humans or the properties of construction materials. Here lies the link with science.

The Relationship of Science to Technology

For very young children, subject barriers may be non-existent. When designing and making a new toy for a friend, a child is using skills from many different curriculum areas, language and mathematical skills, aesthetic and craft skills.

The ASE believes that science and technology are 'inextricably interwoven' and that the relationship between them is a 'natural' one, but their characteristics are 'distinctive'. Science helps to inform the design process in particular. Knowledge of materials helps children with choosing what to use in their toy for a friend. Greater opportunities for technological creativity are possible when children use their scientific knowledge of, for example, how materials can be strengthened or changed, how to use electricity, magnetism or the effects of the forces they have explored. The contribution of science to technology and, through making models to explore phenomena, of technology to science learning, can be seen across both the science and the design and technology curricula.

Fields of Knowledge

Among the areas of knowledge for primary design and technology – control, health and safety, materials and components, quality, structure and systems, for example, there are connections with the science curriculum.

Practical Tasks

The development of children's skills through practical tasks is central to both subjects. Science offers a formal way of understanding more about the world; technology offers ways of tackling a practical challenge and finding solutions through the manipulation of materials.

Investigative, Disassembly and Evaluative Activities

In this area, science offers technology a practical and effective way of testing innovations; investigating the strength of bridges made of different designs or materials, for example, or comparing the structure and performance of model aeroplanes.

Communication

Both science and technology are concerned with the communication of information, drawing, recording, managing and presenting information. In both subjects, children are likely to work in teams, to share ideas and produce reports or artefacts on the outcomes. Both make a valuable contribution to children's general literacy and mathematical skills.

Developing Values

Neither subject is value-free, whether it is the aesthetic aspect of a scientific observation or a technological product, the economic impact of a scientific discovery or technological change or the social and moral issues related to innovation. Both subjects are rich contexts for children to explore issues related to social, moral, spiritual and cultural education.

Industry Links

Both subjects are concerned with industry and wealth-creation. It is through the application of science and technology that we have the resources to make our lives more comfortable, healthier and more enjoyable – indeed, richer in every respect. The industrial uses of science and technology add to the relevance of both subjects. (See also Chapter 2.8.)

What Next for Design and Technology?

The National Curriculum for D & T had a difficult birth and its childhood has been far from trouble free. This most human of subjects, combining head, hand and heart, contributes more to other subjects as it becomes more firmly established in schools. For this to continue, it is necessary to establish what are the essentials of the subject and refine the curriculum to establish them firmly. It may be necessary, in the primary curriculum, to reduce the complexity of materials the children use, enhance the relevance of activities for children and develop the literacy, numeracy and information technology skills associated with design and technology.

Curriculum requirements will continue to evolve; in order to retain a broad and balanced D & T curriculum, an understanding of its essential elements is needed, these include:

- understanding and use of materials
- knowledge and understanding of tools, techniques, processes and safety in order to design and make to meet a purpose
- a core knowledge and understanding of structures, simple mechanisms and control
- a disposition to explore ideas and take risks to realise imagined solutions.

Trainer Technology – a Case Study

A project on training shoes involved one rural school in combining science, design and technology, art and physical education and a study of a successful local industry.

Training shoes are of interest, as fashion items, to many junior children. The school encouraged a mixed-age class of upper primary children to use their trainers as a starting point for this wide-ranging project. One of the units in the SATIS 8–14 project (ASE, 1994) contains materials on Trainer Technology which offers information on the purpose, structure and evaluation of training shoes together with the advice of an international trainer manufacturer.

The study began with an exploration of the movement of muscle and bone systems involved in how the human body moves – jumps, lands and absorbs shock. The forces involved demand that shoes are resilient, shock absorbent and hard-wearing. The children used a shoe which had been sawn in half from toe to heel to examine the way different materials are assembled and joined to make good quality running shoes. They used this knowledge to design shoes of their own, to test a range of shoes for shock-absorbency and grip qualities and to develop a 'best-buy' list of shoes for special purposes.

The work included:

- Life science – body structure, muscles and bones, joints, the nervous system and the skin.
- Art – shoe design, packaging and advertising, colours and materials.
- Physical education – moving, running, jumping and landing.
- Health education – physical exercise and body care.
- Experimental science – the properties of materials, testing for grip and waterproofing qualities, the exploration of shock absorbent properties.
- Technology – modelling the foot, exploring the use of adhesives, modelling the skeleton, suggesting and attempting improvements of the training shoe design.

Some of the social and economic spin-offs include a clearer understanding of the part played on the market by fashion, the real advantages played by improved design and a greater awareness of value for money. While testing the shoes the children found out more about themselves, and science and technology were combined in a way which enhanced them both.

About the Author

John Stringer is a writer and INSET trainer in primary science and technology. He is an author of Star Science and Ginn Science, and directed the ASE SATIS 8–14 project.

References and Further Reading

Wolpert, Lewis (1997) *Science and Common Sense. SPA Journal*, Summer 1997, British Association for the Advancement of Science.

Wolpert, Lewis (1992) *The Unnatural Nature of Science*. London, Faber and Faber Limited.

DATA (Design and Technology Association) (1997) *DATA's initial thoughts on the National Curriculum Review; a consultation document*. Wellesbourne, Warwickshire, DATA.

Acknowledgement

Fig 2.7A is adapted from Ginn Technology (1991) by Carolyn Goodhew, Ronald Lewin and John Stringer, published by Ginn and Co Ltd.

2.8 Science and Industry Partnerships

Rosemary Feasey

Towards the end of twenty-first century the industrial base of developed countries is increasing in its diversity. It ranges from electronics to supermarkets, leisure, tourism and agriculture to telecommunications and hospitals. It includes large pharmaceutical companies employing thousands of people and small businesses employing as few as five. The once smokey landscape spoiled by pit heaps has, in many places, been replaced by landscaped industrial parks specially designed with low-level buildings and high-tech facilities.

Yet many young children in England hold out-dated views of industry, with mental pictures of Dickensian factories and tedious and dangerous jobs. At the same time, many teachers new to the profession hold equally biased views. Does it matter that children and their teachers hold anti-industry views? This chapter explores the views of children and teachers and argues that industry has an important role to play in science education in the primary school. It aims to provide a rationale for science–industry partnerships and strategies for making successful links to support science in the classroom.

Industry is:

> *De-personalising, self-seeking, boorish place to work.* (Student teacher, 1997)

> *Dull and monotonous…, …has water running down walls and rats…* (10 year old, 1997, Thomas Swan Project)

Why Make Links with Industry in Science?

Science and industry links have yet to become an established part of science teaching in all primary schools, which is surprising given the that industry is one of the richest resources on offer to schools for developing a range of understanding in science. Early work in this area by Duncan (1988) and others, indicates that teachers attending the first national schools–industry conference thought that links would help children to:

> *… understand the structure of industry relate school learning to world of work know industry creates wealth…* (p 6)

Duncan (1988) also suggested that:

> *A further justification for the 'world of work' having a place in the education of the primary school is that it helps relate aspects of what they learn in school to the world outside the classroom.*

Today the rationale for developing education–industry partnerships encompasses those early ideas and current links. These are based on an appreciation that, where schools are engaged in links with industry, children are able to develop an understanding of how science influences everyday life and how people engaged in different occupations use science. Children also come to appreciate the nature of manufacturing and many of the stereotypical images are broken down.

Children's and Teachers' Perceptions of Industry

Children's ideas are often based on how industry is portrayed by the media. For example, news broadcasts report on industry only when there is an accident, in drama programmes, police chase villains through derelict factories, and many stories and plays are set in the Victorian era. These images are powerful and as the following illustrations show, children's perceptions are often at odds with the reality of modern industry.

Interestingly, like children, not all aspiring teachers are predisposed towards industry, some student teachers hold a range of views some of which are distinctly negative.

> *If my opinion of industry sounds a little ignorant, that probably is because it is really. I do not feel I have enough knowledge about industry.*

> *I will always avoid 'big' industry. It may be a huge employer, but the environmental issues are huge and very depressing, especially when so many of my pupils are asthmatic. Big industry destroys communities, and has created a generation of ill children. Creating a 'conservation area' does not compensate for this.* (Feasey, 1998)

Developing science–industry links is dependent on teachers who understand not only the range of perceptions held by children but also the potential of science–industry links and how the effort made by liaising with one or more industries can pay ample dividends.

The aim is not for teachers to hold a 'rosy' view of industry, but that they should understand the importance of allowing young children access to industry, for industry forms the basis of our economic and social fabric. Neither is the aim to create future generations of adults who hold naive views of industry and see it as unproblematic. Quite the opposite, the aim is to develop people who can apply their science to everyday life, learn to understand industry and who either take their place in industry or indeed, challenge industry to ensure its accountability to the public.

What Does Industry Get out of Science–Education Links?

Industrialists, with an eye on the future, are not necessarily looking for research scientists for the number of people employed in this role is very small. However, many of today's jobs involve people in using science or scientific equipment.

Fig 2.8A Illustrations of industry from the Thomas Swan Project developed by the Chemical Industry Education Centre (CIEC) at York University

10. | Draw a person who works in this place. | What is this person's job? molding and ● heating

List other jobs that are done in this place:

making glass

11. Which job would you like to do at this place? I don't think I will like to do ~~that~~ any of the jobs.

11b. Why? because its pobibably boring and its dirty and it wont be a nice job for asmatics.

12. Circle the words which describe what you think it would be like to do this job. Add words which you think are missing.

easy	hard	fun
exciting	boring	dull
dirty	angry.	sad

103

10. | Draw a person who works in this place. | What is this person's job?

Seiled plastic
moulder

List other jobs that are done in this place:

Dont
knocu

11. Which job would you like to do at this place? _____

Dont knocu

11b. Why? _____ _Dont knocu_ _____

12. Circle the words which describe what you think it would be like to do this job. Add words which you think are missing.

easy	hard	fun
exciting	boring	un Safe
Safe	terribal	dificult

cannot count

scarey

5

7. Draw two pictures: one of the inside and one of the outside of the place where plastics are made.

a. Outside

b. Inside

7. Draw two pictures: one of the inside and one of the outside of the place where plastics are made.

a. Outside

b. Inside

3

Industrialists value a scientifically literate work-force, they value the skills and ways of thinking, in particular problem-solving, and recognise the importance of 'catching them young'. Equally, they recognise that there are many stereotypes to be broken down and that the primary school, where children's ideas are being formed, is an important place to begin.

Science–industry partnerships allow industry to develop:

* knowledge of the science curriculum in schools
* opportunities for professional development for their employees, allowing them to manage a schools project and work with a range of people
* positive links with the local community
* a positive public understanding of industry
* positive attitudes in young people which encourage them to choose industry as a career.

Developing Successful Science–Industry Partnerships

The key to developing school science–industry links is that each side sees it as an equal partnership, one in which both parties hasve something to offer. The Chemical Industry Education Centre (CIEC) has long experience of developing and supporting science–industry links.

Central to their work is an understanding that:

> *Many partnerships either never get started, or fail early on because the parties did not have a clear enough understanding of what each was expected to contribute. It is very important that this is established at the outset.* (CIEC 1995, p 20)

Linking with industry takes time and planning. The following are suggested key steps in the process.

* Plan the science topic and identify possible areas where links with industry would support the development of children's knowledge and understanding in science.
* Identify a local industry.
* Make a list of your reasons for wanting to link with the industry.
* Find out about the industry. Consider what type of links you want to establish.
* What is it that you think industry has to offer?
* Are you looking for short or long term partnership?

Making Contact

For most schools, the most appropriate industries to develop links with are those within their local community. Making initial contact is often the hardest part of developing a partnership, but it is often made easier if local routes such as parents or 'friends of the school' are used.

When attempting to establish contact:

* Try to find out who in the company has the remit for educational links and would deal with your request.

- Don't be put off if you cannot contact the industrialist immediately. Find out when he/she will be available to talk.
- Have a prompt-sheet with ideas, etc., when telephoning and think through what you want to say.
- Arrange a meeting to discuss your ideas and listen to suggestions from your industry partner, use their expertise.
- Be realistic and be ready to compromise and change your plans.

What Kind of Activities Can Industry Support?

Scientists/Industrialists in the Classroom

Many industries are willing to allow employees time to support the teaching of science in the classroom. There are a number of advantages for having someone from industry working alongside a teacher and the children in school.

For example:

- it provides another person to help children with their science
- children have access to an 'expert'
- children have an alternative audience to whom they can communicate their science
- it helps to break down stereotypical images of scientists
- the visitor can sometimes offer alternative resources and equipment not normally available in the classroom.

However, to make this type of partnership successful, ensure that:

- the person from industry is able to communicate with children at their level
- they are involved with planning lessons and activities
- they are aware of formalities, procedures and protocols within the classroom
- they appreciate their role.

Neighbourhood Engineers

Neighbourhood engineers are engineers from industry who support the teaching of science in schools. They aim to raise children's awareness of the role and importance of engineering to society and the economy, as well as a potential career for young people.

Neighbourhood engineers can support science teaching in a number of ways, for example they can help to:

- organise site visits to industry
- plan science lessons
- talk to children about aspects of their science work
- develop curriculum materials in science
- set problem-solving challenges to children
- access resources in industry
- organise teacher placements.

Teacher Placements

These are becoming an important link with industry. They range from one day to several weeks. They offer a variety of opportunities, from developing links between an industry and school in science, to creating curriculum material to support science lessons, or learning about the science potential of an industry to gaining ideas for work in the classroom. There are many ways to set up teacher placements, for example, asking for assistance from Training and Enterprise Councils or local Education Business Partnerships, applying for teacher fellowships offered by specific companies such as British Telecom or approaching a local industry to set up a placement.

Teacher–Scientist Network

Teachers and schools are partnered on a one-to-one basis with local research scientists. The partners work together to enhance school science.

The research scientists offer:

- up-to-date information, resources and expertise
- classroom support and ideas
- role models which can help to dispel the usual stereotypes.

The teachers and children offer the research scientists an opportunity to:

- share their ideas and interests
- develop interpersonal skills
- develop communication skills
- gain an insight into primary children's ideas.

Published Resources

Many industries have developed a range of published resources for the teaching of science. Industry has, over the years, changed its approach to the creation of such materials; they are now usually produced in partnership with teachers and are more concerned with delivering the curriculum in innovative ways than selling the industry.

Business Ambassadors

Business ambassadors are usually young employees who are asked to go into schools to work with children on projects ranging from talking about their industry to being a mentor to pupils. Industry sees this as valuable staff development for their employees as well as developing school–science partnerships.

Recycling Schemes

Many schools benefit from science–industry partnerships when the industry partner decides to recycle some of its surplus stock. For example, off-cuts from a paper mill or timber yard can provide useful samples which children can use when exploring materials and their properties in science lessons.

Site Visits

One of the most profitable outcomes of science–industry partnerships is a site visit, where children are able to make sense of their science in real, relevant and motivating contexts. For both the school and industry, site visits have a cost in terms of people's time and energy, both want to realise the potential for teaching and learning and ensure that children have an interesting and enjoyable visit. To ensure a successful visit there is no substitute for careful planning and full and frank consultation between the partners.

From the school's point of view there are some important questions to ask, for example:

- What are the health and safety issues for both workers and pupils?
- What is the maximum number of children allowed on site?
- Are the facilities suitable for young children, e.g. toilets, room to talk to children?
- Which parts of the site will children be able to visit?
- How much of the process will children be able to see (or is it hidden by pipes)?
- Will children be able to engage in practical activity whilst on site?
- Is the person who will lead the visit used to talking to young children? Can he or she translate and explain information at the children's level?
- Will children have access to a range of people to talk to?

Science Area	Examples of Potential Industry Partners
Plant Growth	Garden centre, garden tool manufacturer, local gardeners' club, seed merchant, market gardener, farmer, botanical garden
Animals	Vet, farmer, zoo, pet shop, pet food company, RSPCA, agricultural college
Ourselves	School doctor/nurse, audiometrician, local clinic, hospital, dentist, sport/fitness centre
Materials	Pharmaceutical industry, construction firm, plumber, electrician, clothing and shoe manufacturers, food manufacturer, plastics industry, timber merchant, quarry, engineering company
Electricity	Electrician, electric components industry, electrical goods manufacturer, local electricity company
Forces	Construction company, garage, shipbuilding, sports shoe company, sports centre, ski centre, local highways department, engineering company or university department
Sound	Music shop, local orchestra, organ making company, local radio/TV station, airport
Light	Local electric company, electrical components manufacturer, lighting manufacturer, local authority, highways department, observatory
Earth in Space	Observatory, planetarium

Fig 2.8B Possible science–industry links

Which Science Curriculum Areas Can Be Supported by Industry Partnerships?

Fig 2.8B offers suggestions of the range of industries schools could develop links with in relation to the science curriculum.

Embedding science teaching within industry partnerships is demanding in terms of initial time and energy, but the dividends are great. Science and industry partnerships offer breadth and depth to the curriculum, and provide contexts which illustrate how people use science. They can offer experiences which challenge children to apply and develop their personal knowledge and understanding in science, in contexts which can make science come alive for children.

About the Author

Rosemary Feasey is lecturer in primary science education at the School of Education, University of Durham. She is involved in research and curriculum development in science and an author of a range of science resources for teachers and children.

References and Further Reading

Benfield, E. (1987) *Industry and primary schools: a guide for teachers on industrial visits as a resource.* Hobsons, for Careers Research and Advisory Centre.

Feasey, R. (1998) *Science Teachers' Perceptions of Industry.* Paper in progress.

Smith, D. (Ed) (1998) *Industry in the Primary School Curriculum, Principles and Practice.* London, Falmer Press.

CIEC (1995) *Industry–Education Links In-service Pack.* The University of York.

Parvin, J. (1997) *Views of the Chemical Industry in Primary Schools.* The Thomas Swan Project Paper delivered at the 3rd Summer Conference for Teacher Education in Primary Science – Developing the 'Right Kind of Teacher' in Primary Science. School of Education, University of Durham, July, 1997.

Richmond, P. (1991) *Industry–education readings for science teacher education*: Southampton.

Smith, D. (1988) *Industry in the Primary School Curriculum: Principles and Practice.* London, The Falmer Press.

Useful Contacts

Association for Science Education, College Lane, Hatfield, Hertfordshire AL10 9AA

Chemical Industries Association, Speak Out and Listen! Administration Centre, PO Box 7,Winchcombe, Cheltenham, Glos. GL54 5HY

Chemical Industry Education Centre (CIEC), Department of Chemistry, Univeristy of York, York YO1 5DD

The Engineering Council Regional Organisations (ECROs), The Engineering Council, 10 Maltravers Street, London WC2R 3ER

SECTION 3

Teaching Science

3.1 Schemes of Work

Christopher Smith

In this chapter the scheme of work is defined and its purpose and necessity are demonstrated. The issues which arise when devising a scheme are discussed. The planning process is discussed; long-term, medium-term and short-term plans are examined and examples are given.

Schemes of Work

...steady continuous progress is hampered over time by lack of an effective scheme of work.

Where teaching is poor, planning is imprecise. Plans lack a clear focus and the learning objectives are muddled.

The effectiveness of the scheme of work would be improved if it identified specific activities, matched to the National Curriculum with identified learning outcomes.

...the scheme of work ... supports teachers in providing full coverage of the curriculum ...   these provide a good framework for progression in learning.

...the scheme of work offers a good basis for raising levels of attainment... linking practical, investigative work with conceptual understanding.

(Quoted from Ofsted inspections)

Developing the Scheme of Work

What is a Scheme of Work?
The scheme of work gives the school an agreed programme of work which outlines:

- the content
- the approach
- the teaching and learning, and
- the assessment of science, that will be followed by all teachers in the school.

What Does a Scheme of Work Do?

It provides:

- a planned programme of science work which has clear purposes throughout the key stages
- for continuity of teaching, progression and differentiation for all children in the school.

Why Do We Need a Scheme of Work?

It ensures that:

- Every learner is entitled to a balanced programme of work which extends their knowledge, skills, understanding and attitude towards science.
- There are progressively challenging experiences for all children.
- The individual contributions of successive teachers reflect the common goals, overall aims, and values of school.
- Maximum use is made of the whole staff's expertise in the planning of teaching and learning activities.
- There is planned assessment of work across the year groups and key stages.
- Assessment informs children's future learning and gives valid and reliable information to teachers, children, parents and governors.
- All teachers are involved and feel a degree of ownership of the scheme.

(See Chapter 3.2.)

Issues to be Addressed when Writing a Scheme of Work

A scheme of work should reflect the aims, ethos and approach of the school. There is therefore no 'single approach' for all schools. Many publishers have produced schemes some of which are more useful than others, but none will reflect the values and ethos of a particular school. Schools which purchase schemes and imagine that they are going to be the answer to their problems are usually disappointed. Those who have bought schemes to use alongside and can draw from activities in published schemes, are much more likely to find them satisfactory.

An individual school's approach may be centred on a combination of some or all of these areas:

The teacher	Experiences and activities
The subject	Cross-curricular plans
The topics	The school
The child	

For any combination of these approaches it is necessary to:

- help children to investigate in a scientifically structured way
- challenge children's everyday experiences and ideas

- encourage children to learn about living things, materials and scientific occurrences such as day and night, incubating an egg or melting chocolate
- help children to develop their understanding of key concepts – the 'big ideas' of science, e.g. forces, chemical change, growth.

Planning

Having looked at the scheme of work, it will be obvious that detailed planning is best accomplished through developing the curriculum through Long, Medium and Short-term planning.

The long-term plan will give an overview of what is taught when and for how long, and, at the same time demonstrate how the school fulfills the National Curriculum requirements. It will ensure progression across the key stages, balance across attainment targets within each year, coherence within and between aspects of the curriculum, and continuity between key stages. (See Chapter 3.6.) The outcomes will be that a successful long-term plan will specify the content taught; organise the content into manageable and coherent units of work each with a clear focus for learning; allocate a notional time to teach and assess work and sequence the work into appropriate terms.

Issues to be Considered when Developing the Long-term Plan

Decisions will need to be made on the school's long-term planning. For example:

1. Time and Timing

The amount of time to be allocated to science in each year – usually, a minimum of one and a half hours per week in Key Stage 1 and two hours per week in Key Stage 2. It is also important to decide when science activities take place during the day, sometimes in the morning (when children are more alert), sometimes in the afternoon.

Year	Autumn Term	Spring Term	Summer Term	hours/year
Year R Year 1 Year 2	12 x 1.5 = 18 hours	10 x 1.5 = 15 hours	14 x 1.5 = 21 hours	54 hours total per year
Year 3 Year 4 Year 5 Year 6	12 x 2 = 24 hours	10 x 2 = 20 hours	14 x 2 = 28 hours	72 hours total per year

Fig 3.1A Example of the total time available for teaching science (recommended by the Dearing Report)

There is a need to plan for continuity in science teaching and learning.

There needs to be a continuing programme of science work every term throughout each year, preferably within and across different attainment targets.

There is a need to allocate more time to some 'areas of study' than others, for example magnetism needs a shorter time to teach than electrical circuits and health.

There is a need to plan appropriate times of the year to attempt particular areas of study, for example to coincide with planned field study visits or environmental work.

2. Re-visiting and Reinforcement

There is a need to re-visit an area of study during a key stage. For example the use of a simple switch in electricity might be introduced in Year 3 and re-visited at a higher level in terms of controlling the components in a circuit in Year 5.

There is a need to provide reinforcement in terms of the difficulty of particular areas of study, for example the beginnings of understanding of light in Key Stage 1 and the further development of children's understanding of light in Key Stage 2.

3. Making Connections

- *Connections between science areas of study and topics* – Science areas of study can be linked as part of a topic or left as a mini-topic to run alongside the main topic. It is important that links made within topics are meaningful and not tenuous or artificial.
- *Connections between science areas of study and other subject areas* – Some areas of study in science may be linked with other subject areas, for example work on forces may be linked with structures in design and technology. IT should be linked clearly with work in science. (See Chapter 3.8.) Ways in which science links with literacy and numeracy should be indicated.
- *Connections between different Science areas of study* – Check whether the links between different areas of study are still intact. For example, if 'nutrition' is taught in Year 4 then the rest of the Programme of Study, i.e. 'dental care' could be linked with work on 'health' in Year 5.

There is a danger with 'blocked units' that the continuity of children's learning in Science becomes fragmented.

- *Connections between science areas of study and Sc 1 (investigations)* – Check whether there are enough opportunities for Science 1 investigations throughout each term and year. Individual skills should be developed regularly through many activities and there should be about two whole investigations per term in Key Stage 2. (See Chapter 2.2.)

Not all Science work will be in the form of investigations. Other activities will develop specific skills and processes, knowledge, understanding and attitudes. However, the emphasis of science work should reflect the weighting given to investigations in the National Curriculum.

Look at each area of study in Fig 3.1B in turn, for example: Science Attainment Target 2; Area 1 = Life Processes of Plants.
 Decide on:

- The most appropriate Years to teach each area of study, taking into account the

Science 2 – Life Processes and Living Things.	Science 3 – Materials and their Properties.	Science 4 – Physical Processes.
1. Life processes of plants	14. Properties of materials	21. Electrical devices and appliances
2. Life processes of animals	15. Uses of materials	22. Electrical circuits
3. Structure and movement	16. Classifying materials	23. Forces and motion
4. Blood and circulation	17. Physical changes that can be reversed	24. Other types of forces and their effects
5. Health	18. Chemical changes that cannot be reversed.	25. Light sources and seeing light
6. Nutrition.	19. Separation of mixtures	26. Light and dark
7. Reproduction	20. Dissolving substances and solutions	27. Sound and vibrations
8. Plant growth		28. Hearing sounds
9. Structure of plants		29. The Sun, Earth and Moon
10. Plant reproduction		30. Periodic changes
11. Variation and classification		
12. Adaptation to surroundings		
13. Feeding relationships		

Fig 3.1B The areas of study from the Essex Strands document cross-referenced to National Curriculum Attainment Targets (Science 2–4)

level of difficulty and the connections that can be made.
- The most appropriate term to teach an area of study for example 'Adaptation to Surroundings' in the summer term because of the need to take children outdoors.
- The need to re-visit areas of study to build on previous experience perhaps over a two-year cycle, for example approaches to teaching electricity should be different in Year 3 from Year 5.

These decisions will influence the time needed and frequency of each area of study in the long-term planning grid. (See Fig 3.1C.)
   Enter the areas of study into a planning grid showing which Year and half term each Science area of study will be taught, which ones will be re-visited, which ones can be connected to others and notionally how much time might be spent on each.

The medium-term plan will give learning objectives, preliminary activities, the main activities for accomplishing the learning objectives (including appropriate Sc 1 investigations) and some challenging activities for stretching the more able pupils. It will also give ideas of appropriate assessment strategies.

Year		Autumn term	Hrs		Spring	Hrs		Summer	Hrs
Yr. R		This year will mainly be			This year will mainly be			This year will mainly be	
1.5 hrs		concentrating on science			concentrating on science			concentrating on science	
per		skills through a variety of			skills through a variety of			skills through a variety of	
week		contexts and topic work			contexts and topic work			contexts and topic work	
Total			0			0			0
Yr.1		**Ourselves**			**Grouping materials**			**Forces and motion**	
Cyc 1	2	Life processes of animals	2	14	Properties of materials	7	23	Forces and motion	7
1.5 hrs	3	Structure and movement	5	15	Uses of materials	4	24	Other types of forces	4
per	5	Health	2	16	Classifying materials	4			
week	6	Nutrition	5					**Electricity**	
	7	Animal reproduction	2				21	Electrical devices & applications	2
	11	Variation and classification	2				22	Electrical circuits	8
Total			18			15			21
Yr 2		**Changing materials**			**Plants and animals**			**Re-look at Science**	
Cyc 2	17	Physical changes	7	1	Life processes of plants	3			
2 hrs	18	Chemical changes	7	8	Plant growth	3			
per				9	Plant structure	4	8	Plant growth	3
week		**Sound**					9	Plant structure	3
	27	Sound and vibrations	4		**Light**		10	Plant reproduction	8
	28	Hearing sounds	6	25	Light sources & seeing	6	11	Variation and classification	6
				26	Light and dark	4	12	Adaptation to surroundings	8
Total			24			20			28
Year		Autumn term	Hrs		Spring	Hrs		Summer	Hrs
Yr. 3 4		**Sound**			**How I work**			**Life around us**	
Cyc A	27	Sound and vibrations	6	3	Structure and movement	4	2	Life processes of animals	4
2 hrs	28	Hearing sounds	6	4	Blood and circulation	4	11	Variation and classification	4
per				5	Health - teeth	4	12	Adaptation to surroundings	6
week		**Materials**		6	Nutrition	4		**Electricity**	
	14	Properties of materials	6	7	Animal reproduction	4	16	Classifying materials	4
	15	Uses of materials	6				21	Electrical devices & applications	4
							22	Electrical circuits	6
Total			24			20			28
Yr.3 4		**Changing materials**			**Lights in the sky**			**Plants**	
Cyc B	17	Physical changes	6	25	Light sources & seeing	3	1	Life processes of plants	3
2 hrs	18	Chemical changes	6	26	Light and dark	3	8	Plant growth	4
per				29	The Sun, Earth and Moon etc	4	9	Plant structure	4
week		**Forces and motion**		30	Periodic changes	8	10	Plant reproduction	3
	23	Forces and motion	6				13	Feeding relationships	6
	24	Other types of forces	6					**Mixtures of materials**	
							19	Separation of mixtures	4
							20	Dissolving substances	4
Total			24			18			28
Yr 5&6								**Revision**	14
Cyc A	14	Properties of materials	10	21	Electrical devices & applications	4			
2.5 hrs	15	Uses of materials	8	22	Electrical circuits	8		**Our bodies**	
per	16	Classifying materials	12				3	Structure and movement	3
week							4	Blood and circulation	5
				27	Sound and vibrations	5	5	Health	5
				28	Hearing sounds	8	6	Nutrition	5
							7	Animal reproduction	3
Total			30			25			35
Yr. 5&6								**Revision**	14
Cyc B	23	Forces and motion	8	17	Physical changes	7			
2.5 hrs	24	Other types of forces	8	18	Chemical changes	6	8	Plant growth	3
per				19	Separation of mixtures	6	9	Plant structure	3
week				20	Dissolving substances	6	10	Plant reproduction	3
	25	Light sources & seeing	6				11	Variation and classification	3
	30	Periodic changes	8				12	Adaptation to surroundings	5
							13	Feeding relationships	4
Total			30			25			35

Fig 3.1C Science long-term planning sheet

The correct writing of learning objectives is very important because it will direct both the teaching and assessing of the science. There has been a degree of confusion between a learning objective and a learning outcome. The learning objective is what the teacher intends to enable the child to learn or be able to do at the end of the activity. It is what is hoped children will learn from an activity you have set them or the intention of what a child will be able to do. The learning outcome is the evidence of what the child can do at the end of the activity. It must be assessible or measurable and it may be unexpected. A carefully worded objective therefore is the same as an outcome, the only difference being the intention rather than the actual. (See Chapter 3.2.)

The science scheme of work for a school might well consist of the combination of the long and medium-term plans for the whole school. As medium-term plans are evaluated and revisited so the scheme of work can be updated and improved. Being able to have a format which can be updated on computer using previous experience and ideas from colleagues who have taught that particular area before. (See Figs 3.1D and 3.1E.)

The short-term plan will give the details of the activity within the context chosen by the teacher. It will give details of the content and processes to be taught; differentiation and organisation in the classroom (such as discussion and role play); group investigations, whole-class teaching and individual work; and the learning outcomes.

The nature of lesson planning is such that it is usually individual to the school, the class, the children and the teacher. However, the following questions may be helpful when constructing a short-term plan:

- What do I want the children to learn?
- What will my teaching points be?
- Do my short-term learning objectives reflect and break down those in the medium term and accurately interpret the programme of study?
- What will the children actually do (activities, outcomes or response)?
- How will I organise the learning in my classroom? Is there a range of 'teacher intensive' activities, and purposeful but independent work? (Organisation, grouping, teaching and learning styles, resources. See Chapter 3.7.)
- How will I support the range of learners and their different needs? (Differentiation/targeted groups. See Chapter 3.5.)
- How will I know that they have understood or acquired the new skill or knowledge? (Assessment strategies. See Chapter 3.2.)
- What can this planning and the responses tell me about: other stages of planning; next week's plan; implications for individuals or groups? (Evaluation, implications for future planning, review, evidence.)

The important issue is that the scheme of work needs to be adaptable and flexible so that it can be improved after evaluation. This is most readily done soon after the block has been taught, before successes, issues and mistakes have been forgotten. The record within a medium-term plan of evaluation and improved ideas can only lead to improved teaching and planning for the future. (See Chapter 4.2.)

Science Medium Term Planning Sheet

5.U2

Topic GOOD HEALTH **Year Group 3** **Key Stage 2**

Area of Study Health **Time ___ hrs**
Learning objectives **Science 0 and 1 objectives**

* 1 Can describe how teeth need to be looked after.
* 2 Can describe the effect of various factors (sugar) on the decay of teeth.
3 *Can say how bacteria feed on sugar to make acid which decays teeth.*
4 Can explain the harm micro-organisms do by causing disease and the benefit in breaking down waste
5 Can explain how some harmful effects on the human body are caused by smoking, alcohol and other drugs.

Starting Points	Main activity - inc AT 1 and AT 0	Challenge/extension
Discussion on teeth from babies - teething - milk teeth and adult teeth. Counting own teeth. Drawing different types of teeth and under-standing functions. Collecting toothpaste boxes. Collecting sugary food labels. Sorting foods into good and bad for teeth. Designing promotional posters anti-smoking.	Drawing and labelling a tooth and knowing role of sugar causing plaque and tooth destruction. Knowing importance of cleaning teeth through: 1. h/w cleaning schedule with sparkling certificate at end. 2. Disclosing tablet experiment to reveal plaque. Cleaning teeth and using tablet. 2&3. Investigating effect of sugar on teeth. Soaking teeth in various juices/honey etc. and observing decay. Explaining plaque formation through pictures and write ups off observations. Understanding harm caused by drugs through videos and photos of lungs etc.	Investigating dentist visits and treatments (fillings) etc. Investigating animals teeth shapes and functions. Comparing teeth in 'savoury' solutions to sugary solutions. Experiment proving strength of fluoride using egg/vinegar toothpaste.
Vocabulary Plaque, disclosing tablet, decay, incisors, molars	**Assessment stategies and opportunities** Carry out concept map on teeth, repeat at the end of the unit Select some SAT questions to find out where the gaps are in their knowledge Do a true and false exercise - statements on behaviour which helps you keep healthy.	**Major resources** Disclosing tablets, tooth brushes, and tooth paste Videos ordered on healthy teeth and
Initial Assessment strategy Drawing teeth shapes. Discussing foods bad for teeth.		

Fig 3.1D Science medium-term planning sheet

Instructions for using the Science Medium term planning sheets

Science 0
IT, Safety, Communication & language, recording method, questioning, X-curric themes and contexts, health, environment, etc.)
Science 1 objectives (see sheet)

How are you going to stretch the more able and support those who are struggling.

Major resources that you need to order, borrow or make other arrangements to get hold of.

How are you going to assess what the children know and can do, in terms of formative (assessing as you go along) and summative assessment? (What they know and can do at the end of the topic)
eg: Discussion and questioning, Simple SAT - type tests, Revisiting concept maps, Written work, Sorting true and false statements, quizzes, cartoons, drawing pictures.

What are the activities you are planning for your class which will address the objectives.
Example:
1. the **objective** addressed
   a the activity related to that objective
   b a second activity relating to this objective

6. (Strand number)
.1 (Key Stage)

Key Stage 1
Green (Level W)
Pink italic (Level 1)
Black (Level 2)
Bold blue (level 3)

Key Stage 2
* = **Year 3 and 4**
Bold blue - Level 3
Black italic - Level 4
Red - Level 5

Where are the children at
How will I begin this topic

New vocabulary to be introduced to children

Discussion, quiz, True false, concept map, drawing pictures
Cartoons

Enter number of learning objective in column
eg 1a

Science Planning Sheet

Topic   Year Group   Key Stage

Time   hrs
Science 0 and 1 objectives

Area of Study: NUTRITION
Learning objectives
1 Can say that without things to drink we will get thirsty and eventually would die.
2 Can say that we need food and water for our bodies to stay healthy.
3 Can say that taking exercise is important to health.
4 Can describe the different things we need for a balanced diet.
5 Can say why some foods are healthy and why others are not.

Preliminary activity / Starting Points	Main activity - inc Sci 0 & 1	Support / extension
1a		
1b		Major resource

Vocabulary

Initial Assessment strategy

Assessment strategy / opportunity

Fig 3.1E Instructions for using Science medium-term planning sheets
(A complete version of the whole curriculum is available as shown in the references.)

About the Author

Chris Smith is Science Adviser for the Essex Advisory and Inspection Service. He is responsible for Primary Science in the County. He written a number of books and resources for helping with the teaching of science including the development of a number of computer programs.

References and Further Reading

Smith, C. J. *et al* (1997) *Science Curriculum Handbook.* © Essex County Council.
Smith, C. J. *et al* (1997) *Investigating Science.* © Essex County Council.

Acknowledgements

The author would like to thank Bob Bates and Tracy Goodway (EAIS Science team) for their help in writing this chapter.

3.2 Assessment in the Classroom

Phil Hayes

This chapter discusses the foundations of good assessment in science in a primary school. Strategies and policy are outlined and the key elements of target setting clarified. Ways in which bench-marking information and base-line assessment and value-added analyses may be used are suggested. An important theme running through the chapter is the value of involving children in the assessment process.

Assessment Strategies and Policy

Assessment strategies should be at the heart of teaching and learning. To be effective, the assessment processes used in the classroom should directly affect the teaching and learning strategies used. To be really effective, assessment needs to serve a number of purposes:

1. It should provide information about the progress of children in relation to knowledge, skills and understanding in the National Curriculum in science. This information is needed for several audiences, including the school, the teacher, the child and the parents. This assessment performs a summative function.
2. It should identify where schools need to place emphasis in relation to the next stage of learning for a group of children and, as such, directly influence overall curriculum planning.
3. It should identify specific learning issues for individual children and be the principle aid to target setting used by teachers. This is also important for children with special educational needs as part of writing an Individual Education Plan.
   (Points 2 and 3 are formative aspects of assessment.)

No one assessment strategy can serve all these purposes, so schools need to employ a range of strategies.

Currently, the emphasis is on summative assessment in primary schools. Planning and teaching with assessment in mind – formative assessment – is developing more slowly (see Chapter 1.3). Nevertheless, it is true to say that teachers are forming judgements about the progress of their children throughout their lessons, judgements based on their observations, knowledge of the subject and the children's responses. In addition, many schools consider it important to have an indication of children's attitudes to learning science.

However, in order to have objective and comparative data, schools need a co-ordinated *assessment policy* with a number of key features:

1. It satisfies the statutory requirements of the National Curriculum.
2. There is a central record-keeping system which links to whole-school records for each child. (This may link into a computer system.)
3. Criteria for the assessment of each aspect of science have been shared, moderated and agreed between staff and are applied consistently.
4. It indicates different strategies to be used for assessment.
5. Indicates how, in planning documents, possibly at the medium- or short-term stage, clear learning intentions and learning outcomes are to be defined. For example, learning intentions (objectives) can relate to the National Curriculum or other aims of the school, and outcomes can often be written in terms of work the children will do to demonstrate their learning. (See Chapter 3.1.)
6. It indicates how assessment can be used to find out which aspects of knowledge or skills need to be revisited with individual or groups of children.
7. It includes strategies which enable teachers to reinforce or develop key learning aspects or positive attitudes to learning.
8. It indicates how assessment can be used to plan the next steps in learning for the class.
9. It indicates how to use assessment to evaluate a teacher's own teaching.

The ASE's Assessment Policy (ASE 1997) provides further useful guidance to be borne in mind when constructing a policy:
  Assessment should:

- take into account what is taught and learnt so that it can influence subsequent teaching and learning
- match the needs of the learner
- be flexible and responsive to changing needs
- involve a wide range of methods
- celebrate achievement.

Schools should provide support for assessment by:

- ensuring that assessment by teachers is as valid and reliable as possible
- ensuring that teachers receive appropriate training in assessment
- providing relevant information for those who have a right and need to know
- ensuring a whole school approach encompassing the policies and actions of teachers
- ensuring co-ordination across the curriculum.

Assessing Investigations

National testing does not, currently include assessing investigative work, so it is very important that schools pay due attention to children's progress in developing these processes and skills. (See Chapters 2.2, 2.3 and 3.3) Investigative skills are complex and the degree of difficulty increases significantly if these are assessed through concepts at a corresponding level of complexity. It is often more effective to assess these through less complex concepts in order that the focus of assessment is directed at the investigative work.

Formative and Summative assessment

There is much evidence in this chapter for the increased use of assessment in a formative way to improve learning and teaching. Whilst the main objective of summative assessment is to give information about progress overall at regular, stated intervals, summative data can be used formatively by teachers and pupils to give an indication of general trends in the school or nationally. (See Chapter 3.3.)

Involving Children in Assessment

When they know about and are committed to the processes and outcomes of assessment, and are involved, themselves, with their own progress, children's learning often improves considerably.

Marking

Day-to-day marking of children's work is a key element in providing information about their progress to both the teacher and the individual child. A grade or tick for a piece of work is very commonly given, but the main principle about marking is that is should also be trying to provide children with information about how they could improve. Any school marking strategy should aim to give formative information as well as a summative mark. Children will be better placed to be able to improve their work next time. As well as assessing written work, drawings, charts and oral presentation of various kinds for its scientific content, it should also be assessed for its contribution to the development of literacy and numeracy. In order to manage this effectively, it may be necessary to identify one group of children at a time for such more detailed attention.

Partnership

To be fully effective in involving children as partners in the process, the following check list may be helpful:

1. Do the children know what they are doing?
2. Do they know what the criteria are for their work?
3. Do you provide feedback through written comment, discussion or review, which helps the children to identify how well they have done?
4. Do the children understand how to improve their work and what steps they need to make to do so?
5. Do you agree targets to enable this to happen?

This partnership and commitment to improvement is at the heart of formative assessment.

Target Setting

There are two major aspects to target setting in schools. The first is legislation in the 1997 Education Act which requires schools to set overall targets for improvement in the core subjects of the National Curriculum. Secondly, there are targets within the school which, though linked to whole school targets, relate to subjects, year groups, classes or groups of children. This work is only effective if there is a genuine commitment from all involved – governors, teachers, children and parents. Without this commitment, target setting has less chance of being successful. A high degree of co-ordination, especially at the whole-school stage, is needed to ensure that the correct targets have been identified and communicated.

Target setting for children as individuals or in groups, requires a number of key elements:

1. Comprehensive assessment information to enable targets to be identified.
2. A limited number of short-term and achievable targets agreed with the children.
3. Involvement of parents.
4. Provision within the teaching and curriculum to enable the targets to be achieved.
5. Monitoring and review after an agreed period to determine whether the targets have been achieved and the next stage.

Benchmarking

Benchmarking involves using assessment data to compare schools of similar intake and social profile in order to evaluate the degree of relative improvement achieved. Information for grouping schools is based on the school census form (Form 7) completed annually by all schools. The factors which are used to group schools in Key Stages 1 and 2 are the proportion of children known to be eligible for free school meals and the proportion for whom English is an additional language. Benchmark information is published annually by The Qualifications and Curriculum Authority (QCA). Local Education Authorities may group schools using different criteria, for example, the results of county reading tests. These sources of information may be used as a baseline from which progress over time can be considered and used for the calculation of value-added progress. (See also Chapter 4.2.)

Value-added

Value-added analyses are measures of the relative progress made by children with the same prior attainment. It is one of the areas of greatest growth in the development of assessment in recent years. Originally, it sprang from the need for schools to give some contextualisation of their results in national tests published in the school's prospectus and the Governors' Annual Report to Parents. This has subsequently developed as an instrument for evaluating not only whole school progress, but also progress in individual subjects.

Baseline Assessment

The notion of value-added has resulted in a growth in the use of baseline data by schools. To carry out a value-added analysis, children need to be assessed at the beginning and end of the time over which their progress is to be measured.

The baseline for value-added analysis can vary, it could be taken on entry to full-time education, at the end of Key Stage 1 or at the end of Key Stage 2. It will usually be taken from when the children enter their current school.

A nationally instigated baseline assessment scheme is designed to assess all children starting at primary school. It has two key purposes:

- to provide information to help teachers plan effectively to meet children's individual learning needs, and
- to measure children's attainment, using one or more numerical outcomes which can be used in later value-added analyses of children's progress.

Current schemes cover language and literacy, numeracy and personal and social development, and many schemes also cover scientific development.

Such data enable a school to consider the progress made by year groups, a class or set, or individual children. The information can be used to predict the progress of children and to set targets for them. This can be extremely useful in discussion with the children and their parents as they progress through the school, in terms of whether or not they are working to their potential and the targets needed for future success. Similarly, they can be used by the science subject leader to consider the effectiveness of the science curriculum relative to other subjects.

The use of baseline data and value-added analysis is only really effective if it is considered within a whole-school approach. For example, if children are achieving differently from one subject to another, then questions can be asked about the curriculum and its teaching. In this way, the true potential of the information can be realised. (See Chapters 4.2 and 4.4.)

It is important to accept that the modern era of education places a high degree of accountability on schools and teachers, both from expectations of management as well as from parents and politicians. Assessment data is the principle way of considering this accountability.

About the Author

Phil Hayes is a former Senior Adviser for Curriculum and Assessment, OFSTED Registered Inspector and team inspector for primary and secondary schools. He was member of the ASE Assessment and Examinations Committee for two years and is currently a member of the ASE 11–16 Committee. At present he is head teacher of a large 11–18 Comprehensive School.

References and Further Reading

ASE (1997) *Assessment: A policy statement.* Hatfield, ASE.

Black, P. and Wiliam, D. (1998) Assessment and Classroom Learning. *Assessment in Education* 5, 1.

3.3 KS2 Standard Tests in Science

Mike Schilling

In this chapter the technical and legal requirements for the end of Key Stage 2 science tests are described. The process by which the question items are developed and the people with whom the material is written, trialled and reviewed are summarised.

Background

The National Curriculum was implemented, in England and Wales (for 5- to 7-year-olds in Key Stage 1) in 1989. The first science tests (at KS1) were piloted in 1991 and at KS3 in 1992. These were 'unreported runs'. The Centre for Research in Primary Science and Technology (CRIPSAT) was appointed as part of the Agency for KS2 test development in October 1992 and developed items for the first set of Pilot Tests at KS2, which were administered in May 1993. In 1994, another set of Pilot Tests was administered. Since 1995, CRIPSAT has had the contract, with the School Curriculum and Assessment Authority (SCAA), to develop National Curriculum Science Tests for 11-year-olds in England and Wales.

Requirements

The Agency was required, for 1995 and 1996, to write Tasks to assess Levels 1 and 2 and Tests to assess Levels 3 to 5. A separate Level 6 Test was also required. Teachers decided at which Level their children were operating in science and entered them for the Task or the Test accordingly. Tasks were administered early in the year and marked by the teachers. Some children who performed well in the Task were subsequently entered for the tests. Tests were marked by an external marking agency. In 1997, Tasks were made optional in England, although they remained compulsory in Wales.

The Task

The Task is an orally administered, essentially practical assessment tool, which is designed to be administered by the teacher, working with individual children or with small groups.

Level 3–5 Tests

Two tests (A and B) are designed to take no more than 70 minutes to administer.

They address Levels 3, 4 and 5 in Attainment Targets 2, 3 and 4. Coverage is evenly spread across the three levels and the three ATs with a total of 80 marks.

Level 6 Test

Test C derives from the Key Stage 3 PoS (excluding those areas of teaching which do not extend KS2: Sc3/3, Patterns of Behaviour and Sc4/5, Energy). It is designed to take no more than 30 minutes to administer and generates 30 marks equally distributed across the three ATs.

All assessments are required to test science conceptual knowledge and understanding, as described formally in the Sc2, 3 and 4 Attainment Targets. No assessment of procedural knowledge (Sc1) is required of these summative tests. However, the Introductory section to the Programmes of Study is available for assessment. (See Chapter 1.3.)

The Development Process

The Core Development Team is based at CRIPSAT in the Department of Education at the University of Liverpool. A network of about ten Development Co-ordinators was established to operate throughout England and Wales. Primary teachers, headteachers and advisory teachers were recruited on the basis of their exemplary practice in primary science. They, in turn, were asked to invite three or four colleagues (Development Teachers) locally, to collect and collate records and examples of successful science lessons. These ideas and examples were considered and their potential as pencil and paper assessment items were explored at locally convened meetings – which members of the Core Team would attend, whenever possible. As a result of at least one such meeting each term, the groups submitted material to CRIPSAT, in the form of worksheets, lesson plans and outcomes, children's writing and drawing, the results of investigations including data and photographs and, in some cases, draft questions and mark schemes.

The Core Team then write the draft test materials. The aim is to write a double-page spread of question items with a science-based theme, where the marks across the double page are broadly ramped in increasing difficulty. Because questions tend to be changed through many versions, this drafting is extremely time-consuming and is often undertaken at writing conferences involving development co-ordinators and teachers. The mark for each item has to be based on the KS2 Programmes of Study and a draft mark scheme helps to refine the precise PoS attribution by specifying the criterion for a correct response.

The items are collated and, using Desktop Publishing software, sets of test papers are assembled and first drafts of artwork are commissioned. Sometimes the artwork is drawn; frequently, photographs are used. Informal trials of the items are then undertaken with Y6 (for Levels 3–5) and Year 8 or 9 (for Level 6) children. These trials enable the wording of questions to be refined and, using children's responses, mark schemes to be extended by the inclusion of sample responses which help to define the borderline between acceptable and non-creditworthy responses.

These revised items and mark schemes are then scrutinised by a Vetting Panel which is convened by CRIPSAT and which comprises teachers of primary science and teachers with special needs expertise, in England and Wales. Science education consultants, from the Institutes of Physics and Biology and the Royal Society of Chemistry and the Earth Science Teachers' Association are also consulted at this stage. Comments and suggestions from these groups are then taken, along with the draft assessment material, to a meeting of the Test Review Group, which comprises representatives from the teaching profession, science education, the External Marking Agency and HMI, in England and Wales and which is convened by QCA. At the end of this consultation process, items are identified which can go forward for the first national pre-test, which takes place more than one year before the test for which the items are destined.

The sample of children for the pre-test exercise is randomly selected (by the School Co-ordinating Unit at NFER) from schools throughout England and Wales. A group of consultants is recruited to take this confidential material into each of the schools which agrees to take part in this test of the tests.

Upwards of 800 children tackle each test under secure conditions, at this stage and a group of about 60 teachers is recruited to mark the material. Data from this pre-test performance, including facility values (the percentage of children succeeding on each item) informs the development team about the designated question levels and the appropriateness of the mark schemes.

Further question refinement includes a consideration of the balance of curriculum coverage across Levels and ATs preceding a second national pre-test, for which the papers are as close as possible to those which are proposed for the next round of National Testing. The Task material is subjected to only one round of pre-testing. A set of reserve items is always developed, to be available in case a need for substitution is identified.

When the items for the next year's statutory tests have been confirmed, marker training material is developed, in collaboration with the External Marking Agency, using children's answers from the second pre-test.

Adaptations

In consultation with specialists in the education of children with visual impairment, Braille and Modified Large Print versions are also produced. These modifications sometimes require a change in wording. Response modes (in particular for Braille users) also have to be adapted.

Guidance is also drafted by CRIPSAT, in consultation with specialist teachers of the deaf, on the mediation of the tests to hearing-impaired children, for whom some of the words are unusual (particularly in sign language). Sometimes alternative wording has to be found.

Question Types

The non-statutory Task material for England is to be increasingly investigative and packaged as extended activities (more similar to the Year 4 non-statutory materials). The outcomes are judged by what children do or say, as well as what they write or draw.

For the Level 3–5 tests, the attempt is made to set question in contexts which represent the best practise in KS2 Science classrooms: exploratory and investigative contexts are introduced using real data which are pertinent to the question, for example. The involvement of teachers at the earliest stages of question development means that real data can be collected and illustrations of children actually performing the investigations can be included. Response modes include coded answers, written responses and drawing, with answers either being *generated* or *selected* from those presented on the question page.

At Level 6, the emphasis on practical work is inevitably diminished by the fact that the material is based on the KS3 PoS and cannot be undertaken in the average primary classroom.

Welsh Test Development

Out of two 'Development Co-ordinators' and their respective teams of 'Development Teachers' based in Wales, one of those teams would submit Welsh medium material to the Core Team. This material is then be translated into English as part of the question development process.

The Vetting Panel provides the translator with access to draft material at an early stage, ensuring consultation on words and phrases which might be outside the expected linguistic capability of Welsh speaking eleven year olds.

Once the Test and Task material is ready to go forward for the first national pre-test (English medium), it is translated into Welsh in preparation for the national Welsh medium pre-test which follows immediately after its English counterpart.

CRIPSAT's Co-ordinator for Wales and the official translator take some of the Welsh medium test material into schools, to facilitate direct feedback from children and teachers.

Children's responses to test or task items and consultants' comments on the materials are carefully scrutinised in order to identify any linguistic difficulties that arise following the translation of the material. This informs the development team about Welsh specific issues which need to be addressed, post pre-test.

In 1998, Level 6 testing will cease in Wales but the Level 1 and 2 Task will remain statutory. From 1999, testing in Wales will compromise compulsory materials which cover Levels 2–5. Children will sit the same Level 3–5 Tests as in England, but a Level 2–3 Test specific to Wales replaces the Task. There will be continued assessment of Level 6 through Teacher Assessment.

CRIPSAT has also been appointed as the Agency with responsibility for writing Optional Assessment Materials in Science for Key Stage 1, 2 and 3 in Wales.

About the Author

Mike Schilling worked on primary science research projects and ran 20-day INSET courses at CRIPSAT. He was Project Manager for the 'Standard Tests in science at Key Stage 2' contract with SEAC, SCAA and QCA from October 1992 to December 1997.

Additional material from Dewi Roberts CRIPSAT.

What the KS2 Standard Tests Tell Us about Learning Science

3.4

Terry Russell

In this chapter, some of the technical characteristics of the end of KS2 standard tests for science are briefly described, with a particular focus on the Level 3–5 main tests. The use of information derived from the tests is considered from three perspectives: 1) national performance of Y6 pupils; 2) performance of sub-groups within the Y6 cohort; 3) what the tests can reveal about individual pupils' science understanding.

Background

The end of KS2 Standard Tests for pupils in England and Wales have been administered statutorily in 1995, '96 and '97, following two years of development and 'unreported runs' in 1993 and 1994. These tests have been developed by the Centre for Research in Primary Science and Technology (CRIPSAT) at the University of Liverpool to the very tightly constrained specifications issued by firstly SEAC, then SCAA and currently, QCA. The structure of these tests has taken the form of:

- Tasks to assess levels 1 and 2 (orally administered to small groups of 4–6 pupils)
- Two pencil and paper tests generating 80 marks over 70 minutes to assess levels 3–5
- One Level 6 test for those pupils at KS2 who have had access to the KS3 PoS.

The vast majority of Y6 pupils respond to the level 3–5 tests and this chapter will confine itself to a discussion of their performance.

The Nature of the Level 3–5 Science Tests

The specification for the level 3–5 tests requires that they should assess pupils' knowledge and understanding in Sc.2, 3 and 4. It was the firm requirement from the outset that Experimental and Investigative Science should not be assessed by the standard tests, but would be left to Teacher Assessment. Within the early general socio-political hostility from teachers at what was regarded as the imposition of an unmanageable curriculum and assessment regime, non-inclusion of Sc1 in the tests provoked particular criticism. SCAA negotiated a compromise position which permitted the Test Development Agency (TDA) to address aspects of the Introduction to the KS2 PoS – that which is sometimes referred to a 'Sc. Zero'- in the tests from 1996. This shift permitted the inclusion of Sc1 contexts including data recording and communication which resulted in test questions being better able to reflect classroom practice.

On the more general issue of the validity of pencil and paper methods of assessing science knowledge and understanding, the TDA is unequivocal in its belief that such methods have a role to play. Science learning involves cognitive changes in ways of representing the world as well as the acquisition of performance competence: we expect pupils to reveal some 'Brains on' outcomes as the result of their 'Hands on' classroom experiences. It is reasonable to assume that pencil and paper tests can sample aspects of cognition, and the TDA has, in good faith, constructed instruments to do just that. Equally, we must all be aware that the assessment context – practical or pencil and paper – is likely to have a significant impact on performance.

The 'ideal' distribution of marks in the Level 3–5 tests would have marks distributed evenly across the matrix of nine cells which define Levels 3, 4 and 5 and Science 2, 3 and 4. The distribution is ideal in the sense that the tests only offer 80 (not 81) marks and also in that the marks are never distributed perfectly evenly. (Marks are clustered into questions, this level of coherence being deemed more important that a perfectly even individual mark distribution.)

During the development of test questions, each mark (indicated by a box in the margin in the final test papers) has an unambiguous PoS and Level attribution attached (e.g. Sc 2/1e/L4). The Level codes are removed from the final version of the tests distributed to schools, though the PoS attributions remain.

Each marked point must meet certain performance criteria in order to be included in the test. Items are pre-tested first with small groups of pupils, then with larger samples in a First Pre-Test to ascertain the percentage of pupils at different Levels (as estimated by Teacher Assessment) succeeding in gaining the mark. The slope of facility (the difficulty of the item as indicated by the percentage of pupils gaining the mark) against TA Level is expected to be positive (i.e. moving up from left to right on the graph). (This indicates that the pupil's who are deemed to be the better science performers in their teachers' judgements are indeed the ones more likely to succeed on the item.) In addition, a measure of correlation of performance of one item against all other items in the test package is computed. (This ensures an acceptable level of homogeneity in what is supposed to be a test of KS2 science performance). Fig 3.4A summarises typical item statistics for an item having a Level 4 attribution.

A Second Pre-test of approximately 150% of the material which will appear in the following year's test is administered with a Y6 sample of about a thousand pupils at a time close to the statutory Standard Test administration. This enables the thresholds which define each level of performance in what will be the following year's statutory test to be confirmed by reference to the current year's standard test scores. This procedure is used to maintain year on year comparability of the tests. (The procedure is described in SCAA, 1997a). In addition to these technical measurement procedures, all questions are closely scrutinised by expert panels. A 'Vetting Panel' established by the TDA enables SEN and subject knowledge expertise to contribute to the development process; QCA chairs a Test Review Group at which all aspects of question and test validity are considered, but particularly the manner in which the tests interpret the PoS.

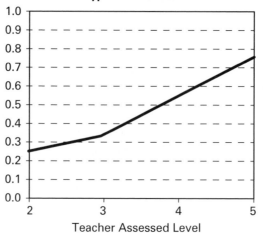

Fig 3.4A Item performance characteristics: Facility by TA Level

Performance Outcomes

What sorts of information can be derived from test performance? Three different levels of analysis will be presented and discussed:

1 National data describing the science performance of the Y6 population in England and Wales.
2 The performance of other sub-groups which we might choose to identify, e.g. by region, gender, LEA, or school.
3 Formative and diagnostic use by teachers to interpret the understanding of the pupils they have taught.

1) National Performance Data

There was some lack of continuity in what was assessed between 1995 and 1996 due to the revision of the curriculum following the Dearing Review. These changes led to the assessment of the revised KS2 science curriculum being slightly more demanding in 1996 – an important consideration in comparing the 1996 results with those of 1995. The evidence summarised in Fig 3.4B suggests that the overall science performance of the Y6 population has improved over the years of statutory assessment. What messages are there here, for teachers? It seems reasonable to assume that these gains are the result of the (primary) teaching profession's efforts. International measures of performance, difficult to interpret though they are, tend to confirm that the primary population in England performs comparatively strongly in science, (TIMMS). Unfashionable though praise directed towards the teaching profession has become in recent years (cite Ofsted), some is due to primary teachers for these achievements.

In addition to the performance statistics published by the DfEE, QCA publishes an annual 'Standards at Key Stage 2' report (e.g. SCAA 1997 b), which summarises

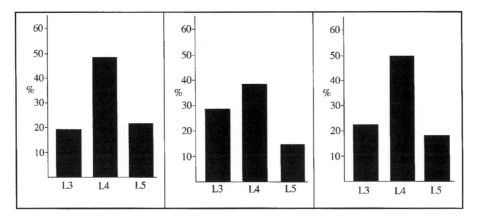

Fig 3.4B Distribution of pupils by level on the KS2 Standard Tests for Science

in 'bullet-point' format some of the strengths and weaknesses in performance of the (almost 600,000) Y6 cohort.

In considering the political agenda of 'raising standards', the teaching profession has to bear in mind the national targets of 80 per cent of pupils achieving Level 4. This represents an interesting shift from a notion of Level 4 as an average level of performance for a pupil at the end of Y6 – the common understanding at the time the national curriculum was introduced. More recently, Level 4 has come to be referred to as, 'the standard expected of 11-year olds (Level 4 or higher), (p 21, SCAA, 1997 b).

2) The Performance of Sub-groups

The political movement in the UK is towards increased regional autonomy, no less in education than in other matters of government. Scotland's and Northern Ireland's curriculum and assessment procedures each have their own unique characteristics. Procedures in Wales differ from those in England in that Level 2 assessment of science remains statutory (using Level 2/3 supported tests). Nor are external tests of Level 6 used in Wales, where Optional Assessment Materials for use at teachers' discretion have received increasing support. To some degree, such decisions have been informed by the Welsh curriculum authority (ACCAC) having reviewed performance in the principality to identify its own priorities and targets, (Welsh Office, 1997). Regional data in England could be analysed in a similar manner.

More controversial are the so-called 'league tables', compiled by the press on the basis of data published by the DfEE, with the rhetoric of supporting schools' accountability and offering information to inform parental choice. Even when 'added value' is taken into account, the mark distribution of any individual school's Y6 cohort does not, in itself, suggest a course of action, even to the best-intentioned staff. The score distribution might be compared with the national average and with similar schools in the locality. If a school intends to set targets of improved test performance, attention to the teaching and learning of science is the way forward.

A school might review performance in each of the Attainment targets, or even question by question to determine areas of stronger and weaker performance. While there will be little time to act on this information with the current Y6 cohort, adjustments could be made to teaching for the children lower down the school. (See Chapters 3.2 and 4.2.)

3) Formative and Diagnostic Use by Teachers

Of course, as TGAT pointed out (DES and Welsh Office 1987), it is not necessary to test every Y6 pupil in the land in order to achieve an estimate of the nation's Y6 level of performance; national performance estimates can be gained much more cheaply and efficiently by sampling the target population. On the other hand, the availability of test results for every pupil means that individual performance can be scrutinised to determine where each pupil has struggled or succeeded in demonstrating understanding of the ideas assessed in the test papers. While the tests are constructed with the priority of generating summative data, the KS2 science tests also lend themselves, to some extent, to formative and diagnostic interpretations of performance. Multiple-choice questions are less useful in yielding such insights. Those questions which more closely reflect practices in schools and demand open responses are more productive for diagnostic purposes. Responses to questions about shadow formation which were posed in 1996 and 1997 illustrate the kind of information which a qualitative scrutiny of pupils' responses is capable of generating. (See Chapter 3.2.)

In the 1996 Test, 'Sun Stick' asked, 'Why does the stick form a shadow when the Sun shines?' In 1997, 'Light' required pupils to, 'Explain how a shadow is formed.' In the first, the light source was the Sun, while in the second, it was a torch. Fig 3.4C shows the correct responses received to the questions.

	'Sun Stick' (1996)			'Light' (1997)		
	L3	L4	L5	L3	L4	L5
Total Correct	15	42	69	18	32	81
object blocks light	8	22	35	12	23	50
object does not let light through	5	10	19	5	16	26
light cannot get to one side	2	3	5	2	3	3
object is 'opaque'	–	3	9	–	3	3
object is 'not transparent'	–	1	1	–	1	–

Fig 3.4C Correct responses to shadow formation questions (percentages by overall level attained).

There is a remarkable correspondence between the results of two different cohorts a year apart, with discernible gains on the part of pupils functioning overall at the highest level. The common erroneous linking of shadow formation to 'reflection' occurred at significant levels in 1996 and 1997. Such stability in the open-ended assessment of conceptual understanding (issues of raising standards apart) speaks for the robustness and reliability of Test items addressing the same conceptual domain, but through considerably different content vehicles. This confirms the possibility of summative tests being written of a quality which can yield formative information. Such formative information can directly inform teaching. (See Chapter 3.2).

About the Author

Terry Russell is Director of the Centre for Research in Primary Science and Technology (CRIPSAT) at the University of Liverpool. A psychologist by background, his major interest is cognitive development and science education.

References and Further Reading

DES and Welsh Office (1987) *National Curriculum Task Group on Assessment and Testing. A Report.* Department of Education and Science and the Welsh Office.

SCAA (1997 a) *External Marking of the 1997 Key Stage 2 Tests.*

SCAA (1997 b) *Standards at Key Stage 2. English, Mathematics and Science.* Report on the 1996 National Curriculum Assessments for 11-year olds.

SCAA (1996) *Report on the 1995 Key Stage 2 Tests and Tasks in English, Mathematics and Science.*

Welsh Office (1997) *Building Excellent Schools Together.* Education White Paper for Wales.

Keys, W., Harris, S. and Fernandes, C. (1996) Third International Mathematics and Science Study. First National Report. National Foundation for Educational Research.

3.5 | **Differentiation**

Stuart Naylor and Brenda Keogh

This chapter attempts to describe differentiation from the teacher's perspective. It stresses the importance of pupil involvement and points out the limitations of an approach based on close matching. A range of alternative strategies is suggested, along with more general factors which contribute to successful differentiation. The importance of keeping expectations to a realistic level is emphasised.

Dickinson and Wright (1993) describe differentiation as 'intervening to make a difference'. They recognise that differences between pupils – such as in their learning capabilities, their prior experience, their preferred learning style and their motivation – make it inevitable that there will be differences in their learning. They suggest that the aim of differentiation is to maximise the potential of each pupil by intervening in the most suitable way.

However maximising the potential of each pupil is easier to describe than to achieve. If differentiation was easy or straightforward then teachers would not be so concerned about it today. The lack of confidence which many teachers feel about how they differentiate is evidence of what a complex challenge it represents. In most classrooms it will not be possible for teachers to plan to meet the learning needs of every individual pupil. It is therefore important for teachers to be realistic in their expectations of what they hope to achieve in order to avoid the disappointment of repeated failure.

Making Sense of Differentiation

Viewing Differentiation as Part of Everyday Teaching

Differentiation is sometimes seen as what we do for pupils who are not typical, such as those with identified learning difficulties. These pupils may be viewed as 'special', requiring a different sort of provision from the rest of the class. The drawback with this view is that differentiation becomes an extra burden on the teacher, something that would not be necessary without those pupils. In reality the research evidence (e.g. Simpson, 1997) shows that differentiation is a concern for all of the pupils, and that it is more helpful to aim to provide a suitable curriculum for all. Russell *et al* (1994) put it bluntly:

> *differentiated practice represents a view of what 'good science teaching' might be – the provision of appropriate teaching/learning experiences for all pupils, not just those at the extremes.* (Russell *et al*, 1994, p 8)

Viewing the Purpose of Differentiation as Differentiated Learning

The purpose of differentiation is to make a difference to the pupils' learning. Sometimes this might require setting different activities for different pupils, but much of the time this may not be necessary. The issue is whether all of the pupils are learning and how much they are learning, not whether the teacher has used a particular approach to differentiation.

Teachers should also recognise that their influence on pupils' learning may be limited. However much we like to think that we are completely in charge in the classroom, this is rarely the case. It is possible to plan the details of the curriculum in advance of the lesson, but it is not possible to plan learning in similar detail. Learning depends on many other factors, such as pupil involvement and motivation, so even if the teacher has planned for differentiated teaching there is no guarantee that differentiated learning will result.

Pupils who are willing partners in learning are more effective learners. If they understand the value of assessment, help to ensure that the teacher has relevant information about their progress and discuss some of the details of their curriculum then they will also enable the teacher to be more effective in providing for differentiated learning. Not all pupils are willing to share this responsibility, and there are no simple solutions to the problems of pupils being alienated by the school culture, indifferent to the opportunities provided or disruptive in the classroom. However our experience is that most pupils are able and willing to share the process of making judgements about their own learning and how it can be enhanced. Giving pupils greater responsibility in their learning frequently leads to greater involvement, increased motivation and better differentiation in learning.

Recognising the Limitations of an Approach Based on Close Matching

Matching the level of difficulty of an activity to the pupil's capability is usually called differentiation by task. This is something that many teachers aim for, but it is not easy to achieve. It is difficult always to get enough relevant information about each pupil's capabilities, and there are practical difficulties in managing the process of matching in a large class. In science there are problems in identifying how progression in understanding of specific scientific concepts develops, and defining the level of difficulty of activities in advance may not be possible. The way that the pupils' existing ideas affect their learning in science is an added complication.

Simpson (1997) found that even teachers identified as being good at differentiation had difficulties in allocating tasks which were appropriate to the pupils' attainment levels. Setting appropriate tasks for the most able pupils has been identified in numerous HMI reports as a particular problem for teachers. Perhaps this is not surprising, since the only evidence that pupils are not being sufficiently challenged may be that they are consistently successful!

In recent years the job of a teacher has become even more demanding. Changes to national curricula and assessment arrangements, inspection processes, large class sizes and a reduction in the support available from advisers combine to make the job more difficult. An emphasis on whole-class teaching is increasingly evident in central government policy. It therefore seems unlikely that teachers will be more effective at matching tasks to individual pupil capabilities in the future than they have been in the past.

So although differentiation by task, based on an analysis of individual learning needs, is an important aim it is not always achievable. Alternatives to differentiation by task are necessary if teachers are to feel confident in their approach. Some of these alternatives are set out in the next section.

Strategies for Differentiation

What many teachers would value is a set of strategies which enables them to build some degree of differentiation into their teaching without having to work even harder than they do already. Fortunately we know that many teachers already use a wide range of relevant differentiation strategies, though these are often used intuitively. The challenge for teachers is to become more aware of what strategies are already in use, to make more conscious decisions about when to differentiate and which strategies they intend to use, and to make differentiation more explicit in their planning.

Sometimes it is claimed that differentiation can be either by task or by outcome. This is unhelpful. Differentiation does not just occur at the planning stage (differentiation by task) or by the end of the activity (differentiation by outcome) – it also goes on during the activity. When pupils are working on an activity their responses will provide important information about the suitability of the task. It is generally possible to adjust the task at that point, making it more challenging for some pupils or more accessible for others.

Summaries of the range of strategies which may be useful are provided by several authors, including Stradling and Saunders (1993), NCC (1993), NIAS (1995) and Naylor and Keogh (1995). These lists emphasise the crucial role of the teacher in interacting with the pupils while they are working.

The kinds of strategies that we have found helpful include the following:

Using a Range of Learning Styles

Sometimes it may be possible for different pupils to cover the same content in different ways, such as using a structured workcard, designing a practical investigation, using a computer simulation or using a textbook for research. Each learning style may be more suited to some pupils than to others. Using a range of learning styles will ensure that no pupils are continually disadvantaged by always using teaching approaches which do not suit them. Although teachers may not be able to meet individual preferences, the ways in which their pupils learn best can be taken into account in offering a broad range of teaching styles.

Taking the Pupils' Ideas into Account

This does not mean planning a different investigation or activity for every pupil! Obviously teachers need to follow a scheme of work and to plan their lessons in advance of finding out the pupils' ideas. However it may be possible to provide an opportunity for pupils to contribute their ideas and then to set up investigations where the purpose is to test out their ideas. In this way the pupils will all be working in the same general area and may well be carrying out similar investigations but with different purposes in mind.

Adjusting the Level of Scientific Skills Required

The level of demand can be influenced by the scientific concepts and the scientific skills involved in an activity. Even if the pupils are working on exactly the same content, the nature of any investigation or experiment can vary for different pupils. Investigations can be made more demanding by involving more factors, building on more extensive background knowledge, using more sophisticated techniques, requiring more careful observation or handling more data. By enabling pupils to design their own investigations, the teacher can provide opportunities for differential learning.

Adjusting the Level of Linguistic Skills Required

Sometimes differentiation is best achieved by adjusting the level of demand in the oral or written language used. The complexity of the text structure, the use of scientific vocabulary, the use of pictorial representation and the use of everyday illustrations will make a difference to how accessible the activity is.

Adjusting the Level of Mathematical Skills Required

Adjusting the level of mathematical demand in an activity can also provide an effective means of differentiation. The degree of precision in measurement, the level of quantification in observation or analysis of observations, the use of units or symbols and the scale of any numbers involved can make a difference to how accessible or challenging pupils will find the activity.

Varying the Amount and Nature of Teacher Intervention

Pupils vary in the amount and type of support that they need to be successful in scientific activities. Sensitive teachers will take this into account. They will try to offer early support to the pupils who are slow starters, to provide extra guidance to those who lack confidence and carefully monitor those who are easily distracted. Clearly teacher intervention is more likely to be appropriate when the teacher knows the pupils well.

Varying the Distribution of Teacher Time

The teacher's time is the most important learning resource available to the pupils. It seems surprising that teachers usually carefully plan the distribution of physical resources (mirrors, magnifying glasses, etc.) but may not make any attempt to plan how their time is distributed. It will be helpful to consider whether to target individuals or groups at certain times and whether all pupils get a reasonable share of teacher attention. Attention from other adults, such as support teachers and parents, is also part of this equation and needs careful planning to be effective.

Varying the Degree of Independence Expected

In general the greater the responsibility the pupils are expected to take, the more demanding the activity will be. Science investigations provide many opportunities for pupils to act independently as learners, such as defining the problem, using a range of information sources and evaluating the procedure. Further suggestions for providing opportunities for independence can be found in Jarman, Keogh and Naylor (1994).

Using Suitable Questions

Questioning is probably the most useful form of teacher intervention. Questions can help to identify pupils' existing ideas, map out possibilities for investigations, identify individual learning needs and offer additional challenges. Many teachers are very skilful at targeting particular questions to individual pupils, attempting to match the level of difficulty of the question with the pupil's likely ability to answer successfully. Preparing a range of possible questions in advance can help teachers to intervene more successfully. Harlen (1996) provides useful guidance on questioning styles (see also Chapter 3.7).

Varying the Response Expected

When teachers know pupils reasonably well they tend to differentiate in their expectations of how pupils might respond to a challenge. Whether it is the answer to a question, a plan for an investigation, a piece of text-based research or a set of observations, teachers expect some pupils to produce higher quality work than others. This is evident when teachers are managing discussion to ensure that every pupil's contribution is valued.

Varying the Pace or Sequence of Learning

Pupils can undertake the same set of activities but complete them at different speeds, with or without support from the teacher. Alternatively they may follow a different sequence of activities through a topic. NIAS (1995) provides excellent examples of differentiated pathways through a scheme of work.

Varying the Method of Presentation or Recording

Sometimes the same activities may be presented in different ways to the pupils, e.g. as a problem to solve, as a question or as a procedure to follow. It may be possible to offer a choice of how the pupils engage in an activity so that their preferences can be taken into account. When they engage in an activity they may be able to analyse, record or present information in a variety of ways. The level of detail, accuracy or quantification involved will influence the level of demand.

Providing Suitable Resources

A range of resources can provide additional support or challenge for some pupils. Sometimes pupils may be offered a choice of whether or not they want additional support or challenge. Suitable resources include workcards, reference texts, audio tapes and computer-based material. The only realistic strategy is to adopt a systematic long term approach to generating, obtaining, trading and sharing suitable resources. (See also Chapter 4.3.)

An Illustration from Practice

At Fairway Primary School, Stockport, Phil Beswick has enabled useful progress to be made in relation to differentiation. As head teacher, he is committed to a whole-school approach to development. Several staff meetings have been held to discuss what is meant by differentiation, agree on a working definition and find suitable examples across the keys stages. These staff meetings identified teachers' intervention and questioning as vital for effective differentiation.

Developing questioning skills and intervention strategies therefore became the focus for staff and curriculum development. The nature of teachers' questions was examined, including supportive questions which 'scaffold' the pupils in their learning and challenging questions to take them further. Bloom's Taxonomy was used to identify and create higher order questions, since these were seen as crucial for ensuring that pupils are challenged. Staff changed their approach to planning to take these different questioning styles into account.

The staff also worked together to produce a questioning environment, in which pupils are encouraged to ask and evaluate their own questions. This has involved emphasising questioning on display, using DARTS (Directed Activities Related To Text) to develop the pupils' skills and creating a culture of questioning for a purpose.

The outcome of this development is that staff and pupils are better equipped in their teaching and learning. The learning environment is now more flexible and pupils and teachers have taken on different roles in the teaching and learning process. As differentiation has become more effective, staff expectations of the pupils have become higher.

Differentiating by taking pupils' ideas into account may be viewed as difficult to manage in practice. Increasing numbers of teachers are finding that the use of concept cartoons is a successful differentiation strategy (Keogh and Naylor, 1997).

Fig 3.7A shows what appears to be a simple everyday situation involving a snowman melting. However using the concept cartoon as a basis for discussion and debate reveals that pupils disagree about what will happen. Research evidence confirms that pupils are likely to hold a range of views about heat transfer. This process of finding out the pupils' ideas creates a context and a purpose for them to investigate the situation. Although their investigations may appear similar, they will be matched to their existing ideas – some pupils will be trying to prove that the coat speeds up melting, some that it slows down melting and some that it makes no difference! Pupils who have a better understanding of the situation introduce other relevant factors, such as the ambient temperature, the colour of the coat and whether it has a reflective surface. Although they are investigating the same situation they go about this in a more sophisticated way and take account of a greater variety of factors.

Actively involving pupils and enabling them to contribute their ideas in this way ensures that there is a close connection between their ideas and their investigations. Their ideas are taken into account without the problems of classroom management becoming impossibly complex.

Making Differentiation More Likely

Having a list of strategies is useful. It can help teachers to feel more confident in the approaches that they are already using, broaden the range of approaches available to them and make planning more effective. Only some of these strategies will normally be used at any one time. Teachers therefore need to use their professional judgement to decide which are most likely to be suitable on any particular occasion and to recognise this in their planning and teaching.

Other more general factors are also important in creating a climate in which differentiation is more likely to be successful. They include:

- actively involving pupils in their own learning, so that differentiation is a process negotiated with them rather than something done to them
- involving pupils in the assessment process, so that they realise the value of assessment and work with the teacher to maximise the usefulness of the information available
- creating a questioning climate, so that pupils see the value of questions as starting points for learning and make good use of opportunities to ask their own productive questions
- establishing routines that maximise the pupils' independence as learners, so enabling the teacher to spend more time on monitoring, supporting, challenging and extending their learning rather than simply organising them
- creating a flexible learning environment, so that pupils can be involved in decisions about grouping, timing, sequencing and resourcing and support the teacher's attempt to provide a differentiated learning environment
- creating a supportive classroom climate, so that pupils feel that they are valued individually and that differentiation is a person-centred rather than a curriculum-centred process
- working towards a whole-school approach, so that there is continuity in the approach used as pupils move from one teacher to the next.

These factors describe the classroom climate and the nature of the learning environment. Although they do not require additional resources, they may require significant changes in the ways that some schools and teachers work if differentiation is to be successful.

About the Authors

Brenda Keogh and Stuart Naylor are Lecturers in Science Education at Manchester Metropolitan University, Brenda in the Crewe School of Education and Stuart in the Didsbury School of Education. They both have extensive experience in teacher education, as well as experience in primary and secondary schools as teachers, advisory teachers and technicians. They were members of the ASE Working Party on Continuity and Progression.

References and Further Reading

British Journal of Special Education, (1992), Special issue on differentiation, 19 (1).

Dickinson, C. and Wright, J. (1993) *Differentiation: A Practical Handbook of Classroom Strategies*, Coventry, National Council for Educational Technology.

Harlen, W. (1996). *The Teaching of Science in Primary Schools* (2nd Edition), London, David Fulton.

Jarman, R., Keogh, B. and Naylor, S. (1994) *I've Done This Before: Continuity and Progression in School Science*, Hatfield, ASE.

NCC (1993) *Teaching Science at Key Stages 1 and 2*, York: National Curriculum Council.

Naylor, S. and Keogh, B. (1995) Making Differentiation Manageable, *School Science Review*, Vol 77, No 279, pp 106–110.

NIAS (1995) *The Differentiation Book*, Northants, Northamptonshire Inspection and Advisory Service.

Russell, T., Qualter, A., McGuigan, L. and Hughes, A. (1994). *Evaluation of the Implementation of Science in the National Curriculum at Key Stages 1, 2 and 3. Volume 3: Differentiation,* London, School Curriculum and Assessment Authority.

Simpson, M. (1997) Developing Differentiation Practices: Meeting the Needs of Pupils and Teachers, *The Curriculum Journal*, Vol 1, No 8, pp 85–104.

Stradling, R. and Saunders, L. (1993). Differentiation in Practice: Responding to the Needs of All Pupils. *Educational Research,* No 35, pp 127–137.

Visser, J. (1992) *Differentiation: Making It Work*, Stafford, National Association for Special Educational Needs.

3.6 Progression and Continuity

Hilary Asoko and Ann Squires

Learning and teaching are bound together. A teacher's sense of achievement comes from a recognition that pupils are learning. Pupils' progress is influenced by many factors. Well-informed, effective teaching, within a structure of curricular continuity, is one of the most important.

Introduction

The words progression and continuity are frequently used, often in the same breath and sometimes as if they were interchangeable. It is important, therefore, to clarify the meaning of these terms and to recognise that they are distinct, although inter-related.

Progression relates to the pupil's learning. It describes the personal journey an individual pupil makes in moving through the educational system.

Continuity, on the other hand, is a characteristic of the curriculum and its implementation by the teacher. It operates in the broadest sense and also at the level of the finest detail. It refers to design, both in long-term planning and in lesson planning and it refers to a teacher's informed and sensitive interactions with pupils as a lesson proceeds.

The term 'progression' is sometimes used to describe the ways in which a curriculum is structured and sequenced. Thus people talk about building progression into schemes of work or classroom practice. In essence this relates to challenge rather than to learning. It means first giving pupils things they can easily achieve to build confidence, then increasing the demand of the task or reducing the support provided. This is an aspect of continuity and here 'progression' is used exclusively in relation to pupils' learning.

The link between progression and continuity is strong, but not so strong that our best attempts at continuity can *guarantee* progression. Teachers often feel disappointed, in themselves and in their pupils. However, planning and teaching with a commitment to continuity, both in structure and in detail, is the most effective way to support a pupil's progression and it provides the best chance of achieving successful and satisfying outcomes.

Imagine the start of the school year, with a new class. To the pupils this is another stage on their journey through education. The teacher may be different in many ways, both personal and professional, from the teacher they had last year. The work may make new demands. The pupils will have to adapt and some may find it difficult. The teacher is faced with the task of getting to know the pupils and translating long-term plans into work appropriate for them. Records may provide information about what they 'did' last year and some indication of the strengths and weaknesses of individuals. The teacher has past experience to draw on. When the pupils move on at the end of the year, they should have 'made progress' as a result of the teaching. This means there is a sense of direction to the work. To a large extent, this direction is determined by National Curricula translated into whole school or Key Stage plans. However, plans are made in the ideal world. In reality, however good they are, they need to be adjusted and adapted to suit particular circumstances and requirements. Individual teachers, with their own ideas, values and opinions, adapt and implement plans in relation to individual pupils. If this is not done skilfully some pupils will feel disorientated and confused. They may become disillusioned with the subject. Learning will become a chore and teaching an uphill struggle. If it is done well, pupils will feel confident and interested and prepared to tackle new work. Continuity will be maintained and progression supported. (See Chapter 3.1.)

A Pupil's Progression in Science

Progression in learning science describes the personal journey an individual pupil makes from first experiences of aspects of the physical world to an understanding of it in scientific terms, and an appreciation of the methods, ideas and significance of science. This journey may involve stops and starts, small steps and sudden leaps, wrong turnings and difficulties to overcome. For the pupil, the journey is something of a mystery tour. It is the teacher, who knows where things are leading, who is able to plan an appropriate route and provide help of the right kind, at the right time.

Progression in learning science can take many forms. Within a given context it might involve shifts from being aware that something happens, to being able to make it happen; or from observation, description and comparison to explanation.

For example:

puddles disappear

↓

puddles disappear faster when it is windy

↓

when puddles disappear the water evaporates into the air

↓

puddles disappear faster when it is windy because the air above them does not become saturated with water vapour

Pupils may progress from explanations couched in everyday language to the intelligent use of scientific language. They can come to expect explanations to be supported by evidence and to subject the evidence to rigorous scrutiny. Qualitative descriptions and comparisons may lead to quantitative measurements; explorations give way to investigations and experiments. Ideas used in single contexts become linked to other ideas or are used in wider contexts so that apparently different events are seen as explainable by a single set of ideas. Ideas about evaporation, for example, can be used to explain washing drying, hardening of nail varnish and parts of the water cycle as well as puddles disappearing.

Some steps on the journey are especially difficult. These are the ones which involve the learner in abandoning well-tried and trusted ideas. Whilst some of these ideas can be challenged by physical evidence, it is often the evidence, not the idea, which is disbelieved. Pupils who believe that heavy objects fall faster than lighter ones will not necessarily be convinced by a demonstration. They are likely to see what they expect – that the heaviest object lands first, or they will try hard to find fault with the test in order to hang on to the idea. Here the teacher must challenge the thinking and provide a new perspective from which to view the evidence.

The learner's progression is the cumulative effect of different kinds of learning event, large and small. Some will involve language learning or the development of practical know-how; some will involve extending ideas already held into new contexts or making connections between ideas; some will involve abandoning existing ideas and constructing new ways of accounting for familiar events and phenomena. (See Chapters 1.3 and 2.1.)

Just as a pupil's long term progression is made up of particular learning steps, the teacher's long term provision of curricular continuity is made up of particular elements of support for learning. The teacher's role is to recognise the many different kinds of learning step and to identify and provide the necessary support.

Building Background Knowledge

Much of pupils' early development in science involves taking notice of and discussing an ever-broader range of experiences. A pupil needs confidence to cope with new ideas and experiences. This confidence comes from having a background of familiar things to draw on and the language to talk about them. In a strange context where pupils lack knowledge and experience, they are not in a position to use capabilities which they could easily use elsewhere.

Teaching may, therefore, involve providing key experiences or drawing attention to significant familiar events and stimulating discussion of these so that explanations have meaning. For example, learning about the rotation of the earth as an explanation for day and night is more meaningful to someone who is aware that the sun is not always in the same place in the sky and that darkness is an absence of light.

Some areas of science learning are long-term tasks which both require and develop a broad background knowledge. When studying materials, for example, even young pupils may be well aware of broad categories such as plastic, metal, fabric or wood. However, knowledge and recognition of specific metals or fabrics, or discussion of their properties or origins, demands background knowledge accumulated as a result of exposure to many experiences and pieces of information. The teacher's role is to seize opportunities to develop such knowledge whatever the topic in hand.

Modest Steps in Understanding

A pupil may recognise some examples of metals and know that metals conduct electricity and other materials do not. Here the teacher can open up new possibilities, perhaps that some metals may conduct better than others, or that the length of a wire may have an effect. An existing idea can thus be refined by small steps.

Major Leaps in Understanding

Major leaps in understanding often allow a shift from description of observed events to explanation in terms of abstract ideas and models. Beginning to think about materials in terms of their constituent particles is a leap in understanding. It is a new insight which, once available, can be tried out in a range of contexts. Pupils who have begun to think about particles in the context of sugar dissolving in water might be challenged to consider whether similar ideas might be used to think about puddles drying in the sun. Once such a major leap has been taken, the idea can be refined and developed by thinking about how particles move in relation to one another, or about the different particles in different materials. The teacher's role is to introduce the idea clearly, at the right time and in the right context. In the longer term, opportunities must then be provided to use, reinforce and develop the idea. It is also important for the teacher to know when to stop and to ensure that pupils don't feel that they have lost contact with what they already know.

Constructing Frameworks of Understanding

Science ideas about the world form a coherent framework. Young pupils may not have developed the bigger ideas which apply across many contexts. As understanding develops and ideas become more sophisticated, they also become wider in their application and pupils come to recognise that the ideas used in one context may be equally well applied in another. The ideas about personal energy which young children hold are the starting point for development towards a concept of energy which embraces physical, chemical and biological contexts. The teacher's role is in drawing attention to the wider application of ideas. Relating different contexts, either within science or between science and everyday life, may involve recognising and resolving conflicting ideas.

Relating Ideas to Evidence

Just as pupils learn to distinguish between events and accounts of events, they need to distinguish between their experiences and the ideas they construct to describe and explain these. Progression in learning involves pupils becoming aware of the need to think explicitly about their experiences, to put ideas to the test and to recognise the value of evidence, both positive and negative.

Although pupils can find out what happens in a given situation, the teacher needs to appreciate that the ideas which explain what happens may need to be introduced explicitly. For example, pupils can discover that objects travel further on smooth surfaces than on rough ones. However the ideas about frictional forces which explain this are not self-evident from the activity.

Awareness of Learning

Satisfaction and confidence in learning depend upon an interest both in our own ideas and those of others. We sometimes only know what we think when we hear what we have to say about it. Ideas may only show themselves as inadequate when we start to spell them out to someone else. It is often a discussion of differing views which leads a pupil towards better understanding. Articulating and considering ideas is essential. It is the teacher's role to stimulate interest in the ideas of science as well as its practical experiences, so helping pupils to become aware both of what, and how, they learn.

Curricular Continuity

A teacher may foster curricular continuity in different contexts:

- in terms of planning for and interacting with the pupils they teach
- in contributing to decision making about planning and teaching within school
- in local and inter-school developments
- in formulating national policy.

All of these will eventually impact on individual pupils.

In curriculum planning we need to keep in focus the variety and complexity of the pupil's task. What will make learning easier and what are the barriers which make the task more difficult or even impossible?

The role of the teacher is vital, as guide and mediator between science and the learner. The teacher has made the journey already and guided others through it. The teacher has the professional knowledge and skills to plan experiences and to relate in appropriate ways to pupils as they work.

Planning and Adapting

The logic of the subject may suggest a particular curricular sequence of concepts. Spirals may be built in to ensure revisiting and extending of ideas. In an ideal world we could plan activities which would result, reliably, in smooth progress and desired learning. But planning, particularly for the long term, tends to make assumptions that everyone will start from the same place, bring the same skills and experience, be subject to the same influences and, therefore, respond in the same way. Pupils, though, are individuals and the interactions and interventions of teaching must be responsive to them.

Nevertheless, planning can be informed by past experience and by research evidence. Plans can be adapted to take account of the ideas and experiences, both helpful and otherwise, which pupils are likely to bring to their science learning. National curricula provide guidance on what should be taught, but teachers need to decide how to structure teaching so that pupils' progression is supported. A knowledge of research into children's learning can be helpful here.

Expectations

Research shows the wide range of preconceptions which pupils can hold. It is important to guard against low expectations which may arise from a misinterpretation of this research. Many of the studies have been concerned with thinking and behaviour *in the absence of instruction.* Effective teaching does make a difference. Research can say something about where to begin and the problems which may be encountered but it cannot say what the goals should be. Sometimes the teacher will meet constraints which are unlikely to respond to teaching at that time. It is essential to distinguish such cases from other constraints, such as lack of background knowledge, which can be addressed by appropriate provision.

A Sense of Direction and Purpose

Science tries to understand the physical world through its 'big ideas', its ways of investigating and seeking evidence and its commitment to developing ideas in relation to the evidence.

The big ideas of science are where a pupil's journey is leading; they provide a sense of direction even for the earliest work. A teacher who knows that a long-term aim for pupils is an understanding of motion in terms of outside forces acting on things will, even from an early stage, encourage pupils to notice the surfaces and surroundings of objects. This doesn't mean imposing explanations on the pupil who is not yet receptive, nor does it mean watering down the incomprehensible. It simply means knowing where things are leading and preparing the way.

However, the ideas and skills of science are not ends in themselves; science makes its contribution to society and the lives of individuals. A teacher who shows an enthusiasm for science and its role in society can help pupils to appreciate this.

Record-keeping, Review and Liaison

Successful review and liaison depend upon effective communication of information about pupils' progress, both between pupil and teacher and between teachers. Teachers have to find effective ways for pupils to make explicit their developing understandings and abilities so that their progression can be followed. This will involve discussions with individuals during learning as well as formal assessment procedures. It may include pupils' self-assessment, particularly as pupils develop an interest in their own learning. (See Chapter 3.2.)

Some of the most valuable communications are those informal discussions between colleagues, both within and between schools, about pupils or teaching. More formal written communications document pupils' progress or curriculum plans. Meetings at which curriculum planning and implementation are discussed provide opportunities for practicalities to be decided. They can also allow the sharing of views on issues such as science learning or the aims of science education and help to promote shared goals and a common approach.

What Information is Useful?

Preparing and referring to recorded information is very time-consuming. Providers and users of information should share views as to what it is important. Communications need to be sharply focused, yet detailed enough to avoid misunderstandings.

Information communicated in an abbreviated form may have little use or be open to misinterpretation. References to having 'done air resistance' or to having 'reached level 3' give no indication of the experiences pupils have had or of the deep-seated ideas they may hold.

Joint Initiatives

SCAA indicate that joint activities with a specific focus on curriculum and/or assessment can benefit pupils in the following ways:

- *developing a better sense of the continuous nature of learning from primary through secondary school;*
- *having their previous experiences and achievements recognised and valued;*
- *experiencing appropriately challenging work which builds on skills, knowledge and understanding acquired in previous key stages;*
- *having similarities and connections with prior learning made explicit.*
  (SCAA, 1996, p 13)

Although this advice is given in relation to continuity between Key Stages 2 and 3, it applies equally to other transitions.

Transfer of Records between Schools

As pupils transfer from primary to secondary school, particular efforts are needed to maintain continuity of curriculum and to monitor pupils' progression. The ideal arrangement is when the staff of two schools view continuity as a shared enterprise. The statutory transfer of records will take place in the richness of direct collaboration. Even without the advantage of such a close relationship, primary and secondary schools find benefit in supplementing the statutory transfer of information and SCAA gives guidance on this and other aspects of transfer (SCAA, 1996).

About the Authors

Hilary Asoko taught in schools for many years before becoming a lecturer in Science Education at the University of Leeds. She is involved in the initial and in-service training of teachers and is a member of the Learning in Science Research Group (formerly the Children's Learning in Science Research Group).

Ann Squires co-ordinated the Leeds Middle Years Curriculum Project and the Leeds National Curriculum Science Support Project, later editing materials from the latter for publication as *Making Sense of Secondary Science* (Routledge, 1994). She was a member of the Children's Learning in Science Research Group until her retirement.

References and Further Reading

ASE (1995) *'I've done this before' Continuity and Progression in School Science.* Hatfield, ASE.

SCAA (1996) *Promoting Continuity between Key Stage 2 and Key Stage 3.* London, SCAA.

Lee B., Harris S. and Dickson P. (1995) *Continuity and Progression 5–16: developments in schools.* NFER.

Driver, R., Leach, J., Scott, P. and Wood-Robinson, C. (1994) Progression in students' understanding of science concepts: implications for curriculum planning. *Studies in Science Education,* No 24, pp 75–100.

SPACE (Science Processes and Concepts Exploration) Research Reports.

Evaporation and Condensation (1990), *Growth* (1990), *Light* (1990), *Sound* (1990).

Electricity (1991), *Materials* (1991), *Processes of Life* (1992), *Rocks, Soil and Weather (1992), Earth in Space (1994) Forces, (1998).* Liverpool University Press.

3.7 Effective Questioning in Science

Rosemary Feasey

This chapter justifies questioning in science in relation to the need for a scientifically literate population and considers the role of questioning in science in the primary classroom in developing adults with the ability to question in their everyday life. It considers the role of the teacher as an effective questioner and what constitutes an effective question in science. The focus then shifts to the value of developing children as effective questioners with suggestions for a range of strategies that the teacher can adopt to develop and support a questioning environment in the classroom.

> *There are no foolish questions and no man becomes a fool until he has stopped asking questions.*
>
> (Charles Proteus Steinmetz, 1865–1923; Mackay, 1992)

The Purpose of Questioning in Science

Science depends on questions. It is the way in which human knowledge is taken forward. Should scientists ever stop asking questions then the consequences are unimaginable, progress and understanding of the world would remain static. Society needs a scientifically literate population, one which is able to question. The ability to question is fundamental to that literacy if individuals are to be able to challenge decision-makers, to question the direction of science and to be able to make sense of their world. Feasey (1997) suggests that:

> *In terms of a scientifically literate individual, the ability to question and challenge science and the evidence it presents is crucial if the individual is able to participate in a democracy. A scientifically literate person needs to be an effective questioner, someone who can use his or her knowledge and understanding alongside the ability and confidence to ask the right question at the right time.* (p 54)

To develop a scientifically literate individual questioning needs to be at the centre of teaching and learning from the earliest point of schooling. It is in the early years of education that the foundations of a scientifically literate individual are laid.

For both the child and the scientist, questioning has a fundamental significance. Children ask questions, because it is how they make sense of the world and take their personal knowledge forward. No child should be made to feel a fool for asking a question and every child should be encouraged to develop as an effective questioner. The teacher, therefore, has a crucial role to play and, as Wragg (1992) suggests, questioning is:

156

... a skill that lies right at the heart of the primary teacher's classroom craft.

However, research in questioning over the past 25 years indicates that many teachers find this aspect of their classroom craft difficult. Kerry (1981) reported that teachers asked the majority of questions in the classroom and of those questions less than 8% demanded cognitive reasoning from children. More recent observations by Wragg (1994) tell a similar story, suggesting that pupils in schools are marginalised in terms of opportunities to question and that teachers dominate classroom questioning, and with questions related more to classroom management than children's learning.

Thus the quality and purpose of teacher's questions are themselves called into question. A teacher needs to consider his or her own questioning to ensure that children are given opportunities to become effective questioners and have a suitable role model.

What is an Effective Question?

Wragg (1992) admits that 'the right question at right time is the hardest thing to ask' but goes on to offer a starting point in understanding this complex linguistic form, by suggesting that questioning your own questioning

> *is one of the most valuable steps you can take to improve your own teaching.*

Effective questioning is a synthesis of language and subject knowledge. In the context of science it requires consideration of the linguistic framework of questions in terms of question stems, e.g. why, what, when, how, linked to a specific scientific outcome, which can be linked to process or knowledge. This can be more easily represented in the following way:

Question stem + Science learning outcome = Effective question

Each part of the above equation is essential to an effective question, the key element is the science learning outcome. Without this scientific outcome, teacher's questions cannot take children's understanding in science forward. Feasey and Thompson (1992) comment that:

> *Simplistic though this statement may appear, the reality is that all too frequently, teacher questions in science lack this crucial component. (p 2)*

They also suggest that effective questions demand that the learner 'put on a 'pair of science spectacles', to challenge children to view the question through their own science knowledge and understanding.

Feasey (1994) adds that:

> *There is ... an intimate relationship between the teacher's personal subject knowledge and the ability to deliver the science curriculum. (p 73)*

The point needs to be made clear – where a teacher has sound personal knowledge and understanding of scientific concepts he or she is better able to ask probing questions and make higher cognitive demands of children through the use of effective questions. What constitutes an effective question is therefore partly due to teacher's own knowledge in science. Doing your own science 'homework' is a prerequisite for teachers being able to frame effective questions in science.

Question Types

The previous section indicated that an understanding of the structure of an effective question is important, this section focuses on the idea that questions can have a range of different functions. Harlen (1992) offers a useful starting point for categorising question types. The key overarching issue is the concept of 'fitness for purpose', each question type has a specific purpose and should be used accordingly.

Attention Focusing

Attention to detail whether at macro or micro level is an important aspect of science. The teacher might use attention-focusing questions to support children in their observation of an object or an event. Sometimes this will require the teacher to use a sequencing strategy which demands that children pay attention to detail at different levels, from gross features to fine details. Central to all such questions must be the link to children's own knowledge and understanding in science. The example illustrates a set of questions asked by a teacher to children observing a rotting log in the school grounds.

Examples of attention-focusing questions:
a) How many different colours can you see on the log?
b) What do you think the small orange spots are on the log?
c) Where else have you seen them?
d) If it is fungi, why do you think that they are living on this log?
e) How do you think they got onto the log?

Open and Closed Questions

Although the above set of questions is related to focusing children's attention, the examples can also be used to discuss a range of other issues which Harlen (1992) raises. For example, the use of 'open' and 'closed' questions, both of which are important but have different functions. Closed questions usually lead to a yes or no answer or a 'right' answer, whereas open questions allow for a range of responses. Closed questions can be used to develop familiarity with an object or occurrence, as confidence is developed, open questions can be used to better effect. However as Feasey and Thompson (1992) suggest, an over-reliance on closed questions:

> *... at worst merely offers an invitation to pupils to rehearse the linguistic etiquette of question and answer routines.* (p 2)

Measurement Questions

Measurement is central to science because it provides the basis for much of the evidence from which children make predictions and generalisations, and draw conclusions. The teacher should offer children questions which challenge them to consider what to measure and, where appropriate, to make decisions about the range, scale and the need to repeat measurements to ensure that data is valid. Teachers' questions should also ask children to justify their decisions to provide the teacher with access to children's understanding.

Examples of measurement questions:
a) Why have you decided to use that equipment to measure?
b) Why do you think you need to repeat your measurements?
c) How many measurements will you need to take?
d) How will you record your measurements?
e) What do you think the pattern of your results will be? Why?

Comparison Questions

These are questions which encourage children to compare similarities and differences between objects and events. This type of question should also be used to encourage children to share ideas about their different approaches to investigations, as well as evidence in the form of data.

The importance of encouraging children to share and compare should not be underestimated. It provides a forum in which ideas and understandings are challenged, refined and reinforced. The following set of questions is based in the context of children comparing results from their investigations.

Examples of comparison questions:
a) Why do you think your results are different from the other groups'?
b) How do you think your idea is different from Amy's idea?
c) How are the two sets of results similar?
d) Which of the three ideas do you agree with? Why?

Action Questions

'What happens if...' is typical of questions which lead children to do something, to explore or investigate. It demands that children take action. Action questions can be offered directly by the teacher or inferred through questions displayed on an activity table, area or wall display. A carefully constructed sequence of questions can lead children towards learning through a series of tasks and investigations in an informal setting. A natural extension of modelling questions in this way can be to ask children if they can think of any action questions of their own that they could add for others to try.

The following example is of a set of action questions placed on a science activity area where the topic is magnets.

Examples of action questions:
a) How can you find out which magnet is the strongest?
b) What happens when you put the ends of magnets close to each other?
c) How can you prove that magnets can work through water?
d) How many different action questions can you think of to add to the 'activity area'?

Problem-posing Questions

Problem-posing questions can themselves cause problems. By their nature they can also be action questions and they can also be difficult to frame. Care has to be taken to ensure that the question stem does not result in a closed question. For example, asking the question 'Can you find a way to?...' only requires a 'yes' or 'no' answer, but if the word 'How' is used in the question stem it becomes 'How can you...' and the question is changed to an open question. Unlike the closed example the open question suggests a problem and that there may be a series of choices to make demanding decisions about which is the best approach. The following questions offer children a range of problem solving situations related to cleaning polluted water.

Examples of problem-posing questions:
a) How can you find out what is polluting the water?
b) How can you find a way to clean the dirty water?
c) Which do you think will make the best filter?
d) How can you allow rainwater into the tank but prevent contamination?

The subtlety of the wording of questions should not be underestimated, just one word can change the way in which children respond to a question. Harlen (1992) makes this point when she discusses the difference between a 'subject-centred' question and a 'person-centred' question. She offers the following as an example:

Why do heavy lorries take longer to stop than lighter ones?

and

Why do you think heavy lorries take longer to stop than lighter ones? (p 111)

The difference is only one word – 'think' – which changes the question from one which demands a right answer to one which invites a child to share his or her ideas.

The way a question is asked can be as important as the wording of a question. Body language and voice intonation are all part of the interaction between teacher and child which can either place them in conflict or provide an encouraging and comfortable interchange. Effective questioning can be as much about the way in which the questions are asked, as the words themselves. Rassan (1993) makes this point when he writes:

... what is important is the questions that you are asking and how you go about asking them. (p 10)

An aspect which is frequently overlooked is the idea which Feasey and Thompson (1992) put forward of allowing 'Thinking Time' (p 6). A child needs time to make sense of the question, consider the answer and formulate a response. 'Thinking time' should be part of questioning allowing children a response time before the teacher intervenes. If, after thinking time, the child is unable to respond the teacher might offer a prompt or rephrase the question, thus offering further support to the child.

Questions to Elicit Children's Ideas

Harlen (1992) provides a useful starting point for categorising questions, other types of questions can be posed which relate to cognitive reasoning. Such questions can be used to elicit children's ideas in science but more importantly, are intended to extend and challenge their thinking. For example, questions which ask children to:

- clarify their thinking
- justify their answers
- think forward to what might happen next either in reality or patterns of data
- consider different explanations for what is happening
- explain their ideas and why they think that way.

There are many strategies for eliciting children's ideas, ranging from concept mapping to the more recent classroom innovation of concept cartoons from Keogh and Naylor (1996). The key question when eliciting children's personal understanding must be, 'Why do you think that?'

The following is part of dialogue between teacher and children based on children discussing the concept cartoon in Fig 3.7A.

Fig 3.7A Concept Cartoon (from Keogh and Naylor, 1996, p 32)

T: *Look at the picture and think about what the children are saying. Who do you think is right?*
C1: *'I think that the snowman will melt.'*
C2: *'I don't, because its cold.'*

> C1: *'But the snowman has got his coat on, right. So he will be warm and melt. Your coat keeps you warm doesn't it' (Speaking to C2)*

An important aspect of questioning used to support concept cartoons is that it can be used to generate dialogue between children. Listening to the dialogue between children offers the teacher a window into their ideas. These can then be reinforced or lead to activities to help children to reformulate their understanding. Indeed, peer tutoring and challenging is an extremely powerful approach to changing and developing children's ideas in science. (See also Chapters 1.3 and 2.1.)

Planning for Effective Questioning

The ideal classroom situation would be one where the atmosphere is both conducive to and receptive towards children offering their own questions. However, it takes time and careful planning to develop the questioning atmosphere and the confidence of children. How can the teacher plan and prepare his or her classroom to develop such an environment?

A useful starting point is to carry out an audit of personal practice. The following is a set of audit questions designed to support, as Wragg (1992) suggested, teachers questioning their own questioning.

1. How are children invited to ask questions of their own?
2. How frequently are children asked to generate their own questions?
3. When children offer questions are they given opportunities to answer them?
4. Are 'effective' questions an everyday part of science displays and activity areas?
5. Do children have an area, book, etc. where they can log their own questions?
6. When are questions used to elicit children's understanding?
7. How effective are questions used in feedback sessions?
8. Are teachers' questions part of everyday lesson planning in science?
9. In lesson planning are effective questions recorded for the teacher to use at different stages of the lesson, e.g. in the introduction and in feedback sessions?
10. Have particular aspects of questioning in science been identified for development in planning?

Strategies to Encourage Questions

In responding to an audit there are a number of strategies to use in the classroom to help raise the profile and quality of both the teacher's and the pupil's questions. The following section provides suggestions for supporting children to become confident and effective questioners.

Brainstorming

The main function of brainstorming questions is to spark ideas and to offer children a non-critical framework in which they can practise asking questions. It is usually a free flow of questions which are scribed and might include things that children already know, but the list is not censored by either the teacher or the children.

At the end of the brainstorm, children review the questions. They consider which ones they think they can answer without further work and prioritise or sort the remainder. These become the starting point for a range of activities, investigations, surveys, researching information and carrying out observations. The list can be added to at different times during a topic, and can also provide a focal point for feedback and discussion related to the answers.

Post Boxes

The 'Post Box' method is one which aims to encourage children to ask questions which are not subjected to the teacher's red pen but are still valued. A post box, which could be anything from a humble cardboard box to a red pillar-box or a treasure chest, into which children post their questions. At appropriate points during the day or week the questions are shared with the rest of the class and children are invited to see if they can answer any of them or take a question home to find an answer.

Mobiles, Interactive Tables and Wall Displays

A classroom which has a positive environment towards questioning is one where the profile of questions is high. There are science-based questions at many different points in the classroom. Whether the questions are on a hanging mobile or part of a wall display they should contain both teachers' and children's questions. Groups of questions with a theme might be clustered, leading children through a series of activities, written on different shapes or colour coded to indicate the sequence children should follow. Once answered, the questions around the classroom can be used as a reference point for small group or class feedback. Questions should be introduced over a period of time so that the display evolves and the questions lead children from one set of understanding and experiences to another more challenging area of learning.

A key element of questions which are displayed around the classroom is that they should be interactive, which includes 'minds on' as well as the usual 'hands on'.

Interviews

Science often brings children into contact with 'experts', whether it is a parent who collects rocks or a neighbourhood engineer working in school. Allowing children to interview people in a real life context, develops both their ability to ask appropriate questions and the speaking and listening skills associated with interviewing. Children should be given the opportunity to draft and reformulate their questions prior to the interview and allowed to use a tape recorder, so they can use the information from the interview as a resource for a series of additional activities.

'Parking' questions

Sometimes children ask an interesting science question at an inappropriate time, for example, in a maths lesson or just before going into assembly. A useful idea is to ask children to 'park' their questions, to log them somewhere, so that the child can think about them at a more suitable moment. Children might 'park' questions in an individual or class question book, on index cards or on a special 'Question Board'. The important issue is that the child's question is seen to be valued.

Children Answering Their Own Questions

Answering questions is as important as asking them, children will soon become frustrated and lose interest if they are forever asking questions but rarely given the opportunity to answer them. However, asking questions is often easier than answering them. The teacher might need to adopt strategies to help children to:

• be able to recognise that some questions cannot be answered
• understand that not every question has one correct answer
• appreciate that different questions can be answered in different ways.

Feasey (1994) suggests one approach to helping children analyse their own questions. Children are taught to sort their questions into different categories depending on how they can be answered, for example by:

• using a book
• try it and see
• carrying out an observation
• carrying out an investigation.

For young children, this can be easily accomplished if they write (or have scribed for them) their questions on a piece of paper which is blu-tacked onto the board under an appropriate heading. The children can then answer all of the questions under one heading, e.g. 'book', before moving onto those which require them to, for example, observe something. Children should first decide whether or not they already know the answer.

Older children might create their own 'Twenty questions' list and classify the questions using a coding, for example:

I   = investigate
O   = observe
B   = book (or leaflet, video, etc.)
TS = try it and see

Progression in Questioning

However laudable teachers' attempts are to improve their own questioning techniques and those of the children, the efforts of individual teachers will only have any real impact if they are part of a coordinated effort and placed in the wider context of progression and continuity within the whole school.

Some schools approach this through their language curriculum, creating a set of guidelines and a framework for progression which can be applied across the curriculum in any subject. Other schools develop an organised framework which sets out the expectations for children and teachers in different year groups. Fig 3.7B is a suggested route for progression in science questioning from nursery to Year 6.

Year Group	Suggested Progression
Nursery	Children ask limited range of questions, e.g. why? Children make statements and use intonation to make statements sound like a question. The teacher 'offers back' statement as a question. The teacher models different question types.
Reception	Range of questions asked by children increases. Teacher offers oral and written questions. Teacher is explicit when talking about questions. For example, 'I am going to ask you a question about teddy.' 'Now you ask me a question about teddy.'
Year 1	Children use an increasing range of questions. Class question books help to raise the profile of questions. Children's questions scribed and placed in the books with their answers. An investigations 'Planning House', Feasey, Goldsworthy, Phipps and Stringer (1996), which uses questions to support investigation planning.
Year 2	Children are confident in asking a range of questions. The teacher introduces new question stems, often bans others. For example, children can ask 'How?' questions but not 'Why?' questions. Teacher introduces idea that different questions can be answered in different ways. Question Boards, Post Boxes, etc. used.
Year 3	Children recognise that there are different kinds of questions including those which can form the basis of an investigation. Children to offer their own questions to be investigated, the teacher helps children to reformulate them into 'investigatable' questions.
Year 4	Children use full range of question stems and types. Children suggest how to answer different questions. The teacher encourages children to ask questions in different situations, e.g. discussion, investigations, using secondary data.
Year 5	Children are confident in using questions independently with fewer prompts from the teacher. Children able where appropriate to turn a statement or a question into an 'investigatable' question.
Year 6	Able to ask a range of questions and use different and appropriate methods to answer them. Able to ask 'investigatable' questions. Children use questions to probe and challenge data, ideas and information. The teacher's role has changed to one where questions are used to challenge and extend children's thinking and actions.

Fig 3.7B Progression in science questioning

Effective questioning in science is a complex interrelationship between a number of factors:

- Teachers' knowledge and understanding in science.
- An understanding of the elements of an effective question.
- An appreciation of the range of question types and their 'fitness for purpose'.
- Developing a positive environment for questioning.
- Shifting responsibility for questioning from the teacher to the children.
- The need for a whole-school approach to effective questioning.

Questioning should be thought provoking as well as leading children to action. It allows children to explore their own and other people's understanding and world. The facility to question allows a child to interrogate a CD-ROM or the Internet as well as an object or an idea that someone puts forward. Questions can offer a window into the existing ideas of children as well as a doorway into new under-standing and experiences. The key to all of this is the teacher who views every question as a central and motivating component of science education and who regu-larly questions their own questions in seeking to provide children with a role model of an effective questioner.

About the Author

Rosemary Feasey is lecturer in primary science education at the School of Education, University of Durham. She is involved in research and curriculum development in science and an author of a range of science resources for teachers and children.

References and Further Reading

DES (1975) *A Language for Life.* London, HMSO.

DES (1988) *Report of the Committee of Inquiry into the Teaching of English Language.* London, HMSO.

Edwards, A. E. and Westgate, D. (1987) *An Investigation of Classroom Interaction.* Falmer Press.

Feasey, R. (1997) Thinking and Working Scientifically. In Keith Skamp *Teaching Primary Science* Constructively. Australia, Harecourt Brace.

Feasey, R. and Thompson, L. (1992) *Effective Questioning in Science, Working Paper.* University of Durham.

Feasey, R. (1994) *Science in Action Key Stage 2 Teacher's Book.* Glasgow, Nelson Blackie.

Feasey, Goldsworthy, Phipps and Stringer (1996) *Star Science Scheme.* Aylesbury, Ginn.

Foulds, K. et al (1992) *Investigative Work in Science.* University of Durham.

Harlen, W. (1992) *Studies in Primary Education: The Teaching of Science.* London, David Fulton.

Kerry, T. (1981) *Effective Questioning.* Macmillan.

Keogh, B. and Naylor, S. (1996) *Scientists and Primary Schools – A Practical*

Guide. Cheshire, Millgate House Publishers.

Keogh, B. and Naylor, S. (1997a) *Starting Points for Science*. Sandbach, Cheshire, *Millgate House Publishers*.

Keogh, B. and Naylor, S. (1997b) *Thinking About Science* (set of posters). Sandbach, Cheshire, Millgate House Publishers.

Mackay, A. L. (1992) *A Dictionary of Scientific Quotations*. London, Institute of Physics Publishing.

Rassan, C. C. (1993) *The Second Culture British Science in Crisis – The Scientists Speak Out*. London, The Royal Society.

Sinclair and Coulthard, M. (1975) *Towards an Analysis of Discourse*. Oxford, OUP.

Tizard, B. and Hughes, M. (1975) *Young Children Learning*. London, Fontana.

Wilkinson, L. (Ed) (1982) *Communicating in the Classroom*. London, Academic Press.

Wragg, E. (1992) *Light Shed on Leading Questions*. In *Times Educational Supplement* 21.2.92.

Science and Information Technology

3.8

Stuart Ball

We are often told how computers can be used in science, CD-ROM, Data-logging and Modelling are terms liberally used. But what does that mean for us in the primary class-room? How will it affect the teaching and learning of science in our classrooms? This chapter hopes to shed some light on these questions, based on real classroom activities.

Introduction

Ten years ago I thought that IT in Primary Science didn't have much of a role other than in the use of a word processor or perhaps a database, both of which could be done better with pen and paper, they were time consuming and often ineffective. There just didn't seem to be anything in IT that would set my science teaching alive and so the computer didn't play much of a role in my teaching. Fortunately, (depending on your point of view) IT is not static, it is continually evolving and offering more powerful features that must offer some benefit to children's learning in science. However, IT has a number of drawbacks, its rate of change being one them, and different equipment, a bewildering array of operating procedures and that uncanny knack that computers seem to have to never work the way you want them to. Such difficulties can promote a technophobe culture and are something we could do without. Delivering the primary science curriculum is demanding enough, so why bother with IT? To see the reasons why IT can enhance the teaching and learning of primary science must ask, 'What can IT do for science?'

Primary Science, for many of us, is about asking questions and doing things. IT has to encourage this approach. Unfortunately, a computer is very good at playing a passive role, where it demonstrates, displays or performs repeated set tasks. These have a place in our teaching of science, but are not encompassing the best of both science and IT. I'm interested in what can I do with this computer and its software that will give added value to my science teaching and children's learning. Now! In my classroom!

So what role does IT have in Primary Science? The National Curriculum clearly indicates the requirements for IT and from this we can establish that they need to use IT as a tool to handle and process information, to measure, to communicate and to model their ideas to help answer their questions. This indicates of the type of activities that might take place in the classroom.

To handle information children might use a CD-ROM as a reference and extract information from it. They may enter data they have collected from an investigation into a database or spreadsheet. This would allow them to sort their data, produce tables and plot graphs. By using sensors and data-logging software children can measure a number of variables in an environment and quickly observe the interaction and changes between them. An extension of this is to use control technology to allow changes in one variable to control another.

Children can experience through a wide variety of different software, models of the physical and natural world, in which they can explore and interact. This can involve using specialised simulation programs, a simple spreadsheet or CD-ROM. Children need to be able to communicate their ideas through using a word-processor or graphics program to produce drawings and diagrams. By using the Internet and e-mail children have almost unlimited access to information and the opportunity to share their ideas globally.

Enhancing Learning in Science through IT

IT in Science Investigations

Science investigations play a central role in the primary science curriculum. Such work can be enhanced by the use of an 'Integrated Software Package', which consists of a word-processor, spreadsheet, graphics, database and communications features, e.g. *Microsoft Office, Microsoft Works, Clarisworks* and *Lotus Suite.* Children are able to incorporate text from a word-processor with tables and graphs from a spreadsheet, along with simple graphics. A good example is the format used by *Clarisworks*, it offers a 'virtual piece of paper' which lets children seamlessly change from one section of the program to another with a click of the mouse button. This allows children to focus on the development of science process skills, without the added complications of trying to organise and draw neat tables and line graphs or struggling with repeated readings and calculating averages. This can so often hinder some in their attempts to succeed in science. (See Fig 3.8A.)

When used in a group context, the computer provides a focal point for discussion and debate as the results of an investigation instantly appear as a table or graph, allowing children to quickly get to the point of extrapolating and extending their graphs and drawing conclusions from their results. Yes, this sort of work can be done with pen and pencil, but the selected use of such a program adds a certain incentive and motivation to the work.

CD-ROM in Primary Science

Multimedia CD-ROM is a development which can enrich the use of source materials, but when children find and print out reams of information without any thought to its relevance or meaning, their role as learners can become a passive one. Activities need to be planned which encourage children to ask questions and discuss and edit information. In this way children produce their own reports based the information they consider important and relevant. Many CD-ROM titles include video, animation and sound as well as text and graphics. These can be useful additions to any science work, but an animation of how a circuit works is no replacement for using the real thing. On the other hand, animation of planetary orbits or video

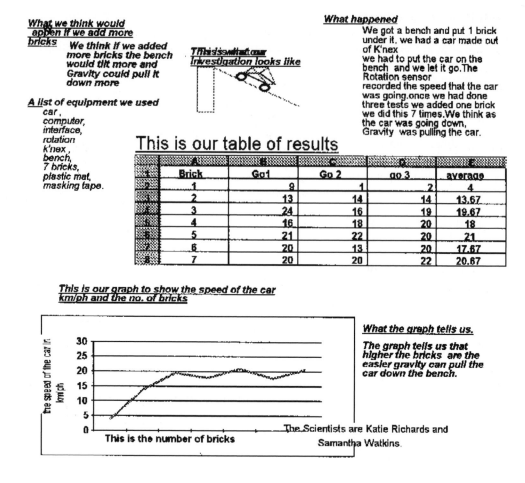

What we think would appen if we add more bricks We think if we added more bricks the bench would tilt more and Gravity could pull it down more

A list of equipment we used car, computer, interface, rotation k'nex, bench, 7 bricks, plastic mat, masking tape.

This is what our Investigation looks like

What happened We got a bench and put 1 brick under it. we had a car made out of K'nex we had to put the car on the bench and we let it go. The Rotation sensor recorded the speed that the car was going.once we had done three tests we added one brick we did this 7 times. We think as the car was going down, Gravity was pulling the car.

This is our table of results

	A Brick	B Go1	C Go 2	D go 3	E average
1	1	9	1	2	4
2	2	13	14	14	13.67
3	3	24	16	19	19.67
4	4	16	18	20	18
5	5	21	22	20	21
6	6	20	13	20	17.67
7	7	20	20	22	20.67

This is our graph to show the speed of the car km/ph and the no. of bricks

the speed of the car in km/ph

30
25
20
15
10
5
0

This is the number of bricks

What the graph tells us. The graph tells us that higher the bricks are the easier gravity can pull the car down the bench.

The Scientists are Katie Richards and Samantha Watkins.

Fig 3.8A An example of a science investigation created using Clarisworks *by Year 6 children*

footage of moon phases would make valuable contributions to any child's understanding of Earth and Space.

There are some excellent CD-ROM titles to choose from. Many publishers offer 'a try before you buy' option this can make choosing a titles less difficult. When choosing, think about it as you would a book for the class. What is the reading level? Is it easy to navigate and explore? Do the multimedia elements enrich rather than distract from the information? Are you able to cut and paste information from the CD-ROM? Are there any additional features? For example, Microsoft's Encarta Series include Interactivities where children can investigate planetary orbits or calculate the nutritional value of their diet. Remember also, that like books, no single CD-ROM will have all the answers and necessary information needed by children in science activities. Children need to become discerning users of the technology, making decisions and asking questions about the information presented before them. They need to interact with the computer. They may even decide that the answer to their question lies in a book.

Modelling in Science

No! This is not walking up and down a laboratory sporting the latest chic white coat and safety goggles! These are programs which allow children to explore and interact with a world that exists 'inside' the computer. The level of interactivity depends on the software you are using. A CD-ROM could allow you to explore a model of the Seashore, a Rainforest or the inside of the Human Body and might include animation and video footage. Some programs have features that allow children to change variables and test ideas, for example a program might simulate a food chain, allowing children to change the number of predators and prey and observe the effects. Others enable children to build 'worlds' for themselves such as in the *My World* series. Adventure programs allow children to explore a variety of 'worlds', solving puzzles in a game type context. Modelling does not just apply to these types of programs, a light or sound sensor can be used as simplified model of the eye or ear. A simple spreadsheet can be used to model situations, as in Fig 3.8B.

How much would I weigh on the Moon ?

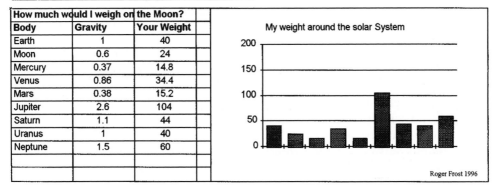

How much would I weigh on the Moon?			
Body	**Gravity**	**Your Weight**	
Earth	1	40	
Moon	0.6	24	
Mercury	0.37	14.8	
Venus	0.86	34.4	
Mars	0.38	15.2	
Jupiter	2.6	104	
Saturn	1.1	44	
Uranus	1	40	
Neptune	1.5	60	

Fig 3.8B

Here children have entered details of the planets onto the spreadsheet, entered a simple formula into the column for weight, that multiplies their weight on earth by the figure for each planet in the gravity column. With a few simple mouse clicks, the new weights are calculated and the graph produced. Children can then take this information and work on it away from the computer and calculate the number of newtons you would exert and plot a graph. They could also try to think of reasons for their results. For example James, aged 10, said:

> *The gravity on Jupiter is more because it is bigger than Earth, the gravity on the Moon is less because it is smaller. But the gravity on Uranus is the same and it is bigger than Earth. So perhaps it is bigger but has less mass.*

This simple activity, which can be done with one computer and a whole Year 6 Class in a day, prompted James to think about the relationship between size and gravity and size and mass. This sort of response is not untypical of children when participating in modelling activities.

Data-logging. To log or not to log? That is the question

Data-logging, is often thought of first where science and IT are concerned. However, it involves connecting new hardware, installing software and learning to use it. There is extra and often substantial cost and it can seem not to be good use of scarce resources.

Nevertheless, once set up and working, data-logging can add an extra dimension to measuring and collecting data not only in the classroom, but remotely, outside on location. For example data can be collected about temperature change or sound levels in different locations around the school. The collection of data allows children to compare and contrast different locations, ask questions and test ideas, so increasing the level at which they can function as independent investigators.

For me, however, the jury is still out on data-logging at primary level.

Can IT develop Scientific Thinking?

In our science teaching we often use some stimulus to encourage children to think scientifically and ask questions. The initiator may be a picture, a book or an artefact on a nature table. Computer software can be used in the same way. I have found some gems, they may not be to everybody's taste, but I have found them to be invaluable.

Life Forms

We have all experienced the scourge of the *tamagotochi* in our classrooms. These 'cyber pets' are simple programs that mimic simple life forms. There are numerous artificial life-form programs available, mainly from suppliers of Shareware (Try before you buy software) or the Internet. The all-time classic is a program called *Life*. Here the children can design simple shapes using various numbers of cells, then, depending on the position of the cell, it will survive, die or reproduce. Investigations can be devised where children are given a limited number of cells and asked to design a shape that is the most successful. This program helps children develop concepts about viruses and bacteria, an area in Sc. 2 which is rather difficult to deal with practically at primary level.

Fractals

Fractals are computer generated complex shapes, based on the concepts involved in Chaos Theory. Surely, a subject beyond primary children. Not so!

A free program called *Fractint* allows children to explore and interact with these shapes. It can be used to develop ideas about the shapes and patterns found in scientific phenomena, such as chromatography, crystals, trees, lightning and ferns. It allows the expression of ideas visually. It also has a number of excellent features that

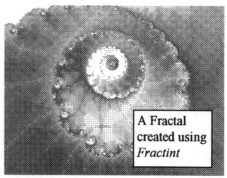

A Fractal created using *Fractint*

Fig 3.8C

let the children make their own fractal landscapes, planets and galaxies, which are ideal for work on Earth and Space. Red and blue glasses, 3D pictures, anamorphic pictures and stereograms are great resources in colour and light topics. This means every child can create their own, making activities more exciting and enjoyable, so encouraging a greater involvement in their science work. It also encourages many cross-curricular links, especially with maths and art.

The Internet – What is it good for?

You may have read some of the hype about the Internet and wondered what on earth has it got to do with me and why should I bother? Firstly, the Government plans to implement the National Grid for Learning, connecting all schools, universities and libraries by the 2002 to a national network. The Internet and electronic communications also open up myriad possibilities for enhancing science work in the primary school.

Briefly, the Internet is a large number of interconnected computers, to which you can connect your computer. You use a 'service provider' which provides the software and the phone number for you to connect to. You also need a modem, which converts the computer signals to a form which can be sent along a phone line. Once connected, you have access to unlimited resources and information.

Surfing is an exciting aspect of the Internet as children can find and discover information for themselves, but they need to have structure and learn how to be specific in their search activities. This can be achieved by using the search or browsing software to 'book mark' specific sites of information or to use a specialised educational service provider such as BT's *Campusworld,* which only allows access to specific areas.

The information contained on the Internet ranges from the simple pages of text to pages of photographs, sound and video clips. In contrast CD-ROM, the information on the Internet is dynamic, information is constantly updated and changing, so weather reports change hourly and pictures from the latest Mars exploration mission are available within hours of them reaching NASA. The flow of information over the Internet is two-way, not only can children access information but they can also contribute to it, by developing their own sites of information, accessing sites that encourage interactivity and communicating through e-mail. Children are able to share their ideas, ask questions of real scientists, control robots and remote telescopes and take part in on-line investigations with schools almost anywhere in the world.

The prospect for developing children's scientific concepts and communicating their ideas over the Internet is extremely exciting and challenging. It is an area that may completely change the way we use IT in the Primary Classroom.

If we are going to make the best use of IT in science, it helps to think of any aspect of IT in the following ways:

- Does it enhance children's learning of science?
- Does it encourage scientific ideas and questioning?
- Does it allow children to develop their own ideas?
- Does it promote learning thorough interactivity?

- Is it easy for teachers and children to use?
- Does it use a common format? *
- Is it reasonably priced?

Summary

In 10 years IT has progressed enormously, but perhaps the use of IT in science in the classroom has not matched that progress. We are now in a position where cheaper equipment and developments in communications can provide a means by which all children can develop their scientific knowledge and understanding, ask questions and communicate their ideas. This can only benefit our teaching and their learning.

Information Technology is a tool that can only be used effectively if the quality of science teaching in our classrooms is good. If it is used well, it will make an important and valuable contribution made to children's learning.

What will the future bring? Who Knows!

About the Author

Stuart Ball is a Year 6 Teacher in Monmouthshire and has specialised in incorporating IT into Science investigative work. He was the 1997 TES Primary Science Teacher of the Year.

References and Further Reading

Ball, S. (1996) Chaos in the Classroom. *Primary Science Review* No 41, pp 3–5.

Frost, Roger (1996) *IT in Primary Science: A compendium of ideas for using computers and teaching science.* IT in Science/ASE.

Frost, Roger (1997) *The Science Teachers' Guide to Computer Software.* A report for the DfEE Science Curriculum IT Support Group. ASE.

DfEE (1997) *Connecting the Learning Society: National Grid for Learning.* Consultation Paper, DfEE.

Welsh Office (1995) *Key Stages 1 and 2 Wales.* HMSO.

Mailer, N. and Dickson, B. (1994) *UK School Internet Primer* Koeksuster Publications.

* Most of the software mentioned here is readily available and runs on PCs under the Windows operating system. This means that the skills learned by children in school are readily transferred to the home and ultimately the work environments.

SECTION 4

Managing Science

Management and Development – Introduction

Mary Ratcliffe

The Professional Development of Teachers

Teacher Development

Effective teaching and learning cannot happen without good teachers of science. The principles and methods of initial teacher education (ITE) and continuing professional development (CPD) are therefore very important.

There are important elements which go towards good science teaching (see Chapter 1.2), yet these elements combine in ways which are difficult to describe.

An atomistic view of teacher development may take an approach which identifies each separate element of teacher knowledge and skill and then seeks to tackle each separately with teachers in training. This atomistic approach has similarities with a strict competency model. Competences underpin the Standards for qualified teacher status (QTS) and the National Curriculum for Initial Teacher Training (ITT) in operation through the Teacher Training Agency (TTA) in England and Wales.

An holistic view of teacher development sees the sum of these elements as greater than the separate parts. Trainee teachers develop knowledge and skills in context, integrating the variety of different experiences as they develop a good understanding and ability of teaching. An holistic view, in assessing teachers' progess, perhaps relies on professional judgement, on knowing quality teaching when you see it and on a standard of entry to the profession based on expert agreed judgement.

Furlong and Maynard (1995) characterise learning to teach as:

> the development of an appropriate body of practical professional knowledge with which student teachers can come to frame actual teaching situations. This body of knowledge is made up of both a stock of concrete experiences as well as more abstract concepts.

They argue that teachers' knowledge falls into four domains – knowledge of pupils, knowledge of strategies, knowledge of content and knowledge of context.

> But teachers' practice does not depend on knowledge from a cluster of discrete domains; rather, it depends on the complex interaction and interplay between these domains. Effective practice, rather like a complex, three dimensional jigsaw puzzle, is only achieved when all the pieces are in place, when there is a sense of 'balance'.

Learning to teach science is thus a complex business and is assisted by activities which allow student teachers to integrate their experience of these four domains.

Initial Teacher Education

In recognising the complex interplay of these knowledge domains, it is still sensible to try to articulate the skills and attributes of beginning teachers. This then provides a basis for further development.

Principles of provision in ITE should be closely linked to achieving the purposes of science education (Chapter 1.1) and high-quality learning in science (Chapter 1.2).

Good initial teacher education should allow new entrants to the profession to:

- be reflective, enthusiastic, flexible, thoughtful and skilled practitioners able to show good pedagogical content knowledge in their teaching
- support pupil learning in science through using 'fitness for purpose' in identifying appropriate learning activities and assessment methods
- progress in their professional development with the support of more experienced colleagues.

ASE, in responding to TTA consultation on the shape of an ITT National Curriculum in Science, argued for the use of key themes in which student teachers can integrate the domains of professional knowledge. These themes can guide the developing expertise of student teachers in supporting pupils' learning and in using appropriate teaching and assessment methods (ASE, 1997a).

Five areas of pupils' development, related to the purposes of science education, are important:

- *The nature of scientific ideas* – generation and evaluation of evidence, science as a human and team endeavour.
- *Systematic enquiry in science* – including conceptual and procedural knowledge, development of practical skills.
- *Science in everyday life* – development of science ideas in context.
- *Communication of scientific ideas* – development of skills of literacy and numeracy in relation to scientific ideas.
- *Health and safety* – understanding and demonstration of safe practice.

Themes for developing student teachers' experience in assisting these areas of pupils' learning include:

a) An understanding of the nature of science including: the role of theories; evidence generation and evidence evaluation; the human context of scientific development.
b) An understanding of the practical processes and skills of science including observation, manipulation, etc.
c) An understanding of how pupils learn in science and an appreciation of the nature of misconceptions in scientific ideas.
d) The use of models in explaining scientific ideas.
e) An understanding of the industrial and community context of science.
f) An understanding and demonstration of good health and safety practices in science.
g) An understanding of the links between science and other subjects, particularly mathematics, technology, information technology and English.

h) Thinking and working scientifically and enthusiastically using appropriate language – i.e. *a synthesis of all the above.*

Each of these themes are discussed in chapters in this book.

Standards for QTS identify what beginning teachers must achieve from a course of initial teacher training in order to enter the profession (DfEE, 1997). These Standards are grouped under headings of:

A) *Knowledge and Understanding*
B) *Planning, Teaching and Class Management*
C) *Monitoring, Assessment, Recording, Reporting and Accountability*
D) *Other Professional Requirements.*

The Standards are detailed – specifying skills, knowledge and attributes which need to be demonstrated before a student teacher can be awarded qualified teacher status.

National Curricula in ITT for the core subjects of English, Mathematics and Science and for ICT support and add further detail to these requirements (TTA, 1998). They specify:

A) *Pedagogical knowledge and understanding required by trainees to secure pupils' progress.*
B) *Effective teaching and assessment methods which trainees must be taught and be able to use.*
C) *Trainees' knowledge and understanding of the subject.*

Interesting issues are raised by the prospect of a National Curriculum in initial teacher education. In particular, the TTA consultation prompted a debate on the nature of subject knowledge needed for teaching science at any particular level. Clearly we cannot teach science without a sound understanding of the subject but this needs to be integrated with other knowledge. However, there seems no consensus on what constitutes a sound understanding of science. Proxy measures such as a GCSE grade 'C' or a PhD in physics give some idea of previous experience and depth of engagement with key ideas of science. We probably come to best realise the extent and use of our subject knowledge when we engage in explaining and teaching. This is as true for people teaching from a background of degree level study in the subject as for those teaching from a lower base. We learn a lot from our own teaching. Use and development of subject knowledge in context seem important principles for ITE and CPD.

Continuing Professional Development

Teacher development should be seen as a continuum. Whatever length of time we have been teaching we continue to learn. ASE:

> *firmly believes that all teachers of science should be entitled to high quality continuing professional development from initial teacher education onwards throughout their career.* (ASE, 1997)

This entitlement also brings with it an obligation for teachers to maintain and improve their professional skills and understanding.

There are obviously many ways in which to engage with professional development opportunities. The management issues outlined in section 4, provide opportunities and challenges in professional development. However, professional development should be coherent and systematic, matching school and individual requirements.

A CPD framework should:

- allow progression from initial training through induction as an NQT to ongoing professional experience
- be meaningful to all who use it – the teacher, mentor, senior management
- be realistic enough to have achievable goals
- be flexible enough to respond to the individual's particular circumstances and ensure that the needs of both the teacher and employer are being met
- be rigorous enough to provide evidence of achievement
- be part of a reflective process to enable individuals to identify their own levels of expertise and further development
- encourage a support system involving an experienced mentor to assist in target setting and monitoring.

One framework for CPD is being piloted by secondary science teachers through an ASE initiative. The potential of the framework lies in giving a structure for needs analysis and identified CPD activities, supported by a more experienced professional as mentor. The ASE framework proposes a number of domains – all being important in professional development. Just as initial teacher education requires a synthesis of different elements, the areas in a CPD framework should not be seen as discrete but overlapping. The framework is to guide and assist coverage of interrelated elements of teacher development and includes the following areas:

- *Pedagogical content knowledge* – examination of the teaching of particular parts of the science curriculum including translation of one's own subject knowledge into suitable classroom activities. This is an overarching area which brings together all the others listed.
- *Subject knowledge* – development of secure understanding in the sciences taught; awareness of recent advances.
- *Practical teaching skills* – development of teaching skills which are felt to be underdeveloped or under-used by the individual. It also includes development in appropriate assessment and evaluation techniques.
- *Theoretical understanding of teaching and learning science* – reflection on the basis for the classroom practice of oneself and of others – How do pupils learn? Why do I teach this way?
- *Knowledge of external changes affecting the teaching of science* – development of knowledge relating to the context of science teaching, e.g. awareness of curriculum policy developments at national level; links with industries; regional and national initiatives in curriculum development.
- *Development of personal skills and attitudes towards science and science teaching* – development of any changing responsibilities, management tasks, extra-curricular activities, etc.

The use of a framework like this may assist teachers in systematic evaluation and development of professional practice. Teachers and managers may find it useful in identifying appropriate CPD activities both within and outside the school. Evidence can be collected of achievement in each area and impact on classroom practice and pupils' learning.

This developmental framework is intended to be a tool to assist ongoing professional development *whatever stage a teacher's career is at*. The TTA take a different approach – setting Standards for different key points of a teacher's career:

- Entry Standards (DfEE, 1997).
- Standards for Subject Expert (in development).
- Standards for Subject Leader (see Chapter 4.1).
- Standards for Headteacher (National Professional Qualification for Head-teacher).

This model of teacher development perhaps assumes a particular career path for most teachers.

Mentors

We are all assisted in our professional development by the support and guidance of a more experienced professional – a mentor. Teachers in training rely on the guidance of the class teacher and head of science for constructive criticism of their developing expertise. Equally, more experienced teachers benefit from the critical guidance of a supportive mentor. Effective mentoring is not easy and may challenge the most expert of teachers. Expert teachers often have intuitive responses to classroom situations:

> *They are acting effortlessly, fluidly, and in a sense this is arational, because it is not easily described as deductive or analytic behaviour.* (Berliner, 1994)

It can be a difficult business to unpick practice, particularly one's own, and explain how the teacher's activities contributed (or not) to effective learning. However, it can be a rewarding learning experience for the mentor as well as the person being guided. Monk and Dillon (1995) provide activities to support the mentoring of inexperienced secondary science teachers. Partnership between schools and Higher Education Institutions can be effective in together providing good support for professional development both in ITE and CPD. Indeed, the ASE believes

> *…that initial science teacher education courses are best provided by partnerships between schools and higher education institutions, with each side of the partnership adopting the role(s) it is best placed to provide.'* (ASE, 1997c)

References

ASE (1997a) National Curriculum for Initial Teacher Training in Science – Response to Consultation June 1997, Hatfield, ASE.

ASE (1997b) *Continuing Professional Development: Policy Statement*, Hatfield, ASE.

ASE (1997c) *Initial Teacher Education: Policy Statement*, Hatfield, ASE.

Berliner, D. (1994) Teacher Expertise. In Moon, B. and Shelton Mayes, A. (Eds) *Teaching and Learning in the Secondary School,* London, Routledge/Open University Press, pp 107–113.

DfEE (1997) *Circular 10/97, Requirements for Courses of Initial Teacher Training.*

Furlong, J. and Maynard, T. (1995) *Mentoring Student Teachers*, London, Routledge.

Monk, M. and Dillon, J. (1995) *Learning to Teach Science: Activities for Student Teachers and Mentors,* London, Falmer Press.

TTA (1998) *ITT National Curriculum for Primary Science, ITT National Curriculum for Secondary Science Consultation Draft.*

From Science Co-ordinator to Science Subject Leader

Ron Ritchie

This chapter addresses the important role of the primary science co-ordinator and how it is developing into a subject leadership role. The National Framework, established by the TTA for Subject Leaders, is outlined. Recent research findings are used to illustrate the current situation, indicating what co-ordinators are actually doing, what support they get and the constraints on their role. The challenges faced by co-ordinators are then explored. Several of these are amplified in later chapters in this section. The chapter concludes with a plea for co-ordinators to recognise the part they can play in contributing to the development of a new science curriculum for the new millennium.

Science is a National Curriculum success story and that success, at least in part, is due to the efforts of science co-ordinators. Since the introduction of a statutory science curriculum co-ordinators have been supporting colleagues in 'making it work' (Ollerenshaw and Ritchie, 1997). Their tasks have included writing policies, organising whole staff discussions about planning and schemes of work, providing staff development through INSET days, giving advice, keeping up to date with the latest curriculum documents/guidance and purchasing and organising resources. It has not been an easy job. One of the problems facing co-ordinators has been their colleagues' (and sometimes, their own) lack of subject knowledge and confidence to teach science through practical exploration and investigations. Additionally, finding time to do the job properly and take on the 'management' aspects needed to change practice in schools has been difficult.

In the last few years, further expectations have been placed on co-ordinators. OFSTED inspections, and the increasing emphasis on accountability, standards and pupil achievement (as highlighted in the White Paper, Excellence in Education (DfEE, 1997) have required greater emphasis to be placed on monitoring, evaluation and target setting. The somewhat ad hoc nature of the co-ordinators' roles and responsibilities, which varied from school to school, is being clarified. The TTA National Standards (published in July 1997) provide a comprehensive, and generally accepted (if somewhat idealistic), view of what is required. Indeed, the science co-ordinator role has evolved into subject leader role (Bell and Ritchie, 1998). This implies a more proactive approach. The subject leader is expected to set the strategic direction for science (in collaboration with the headteacher and in the context of whole school planning), provide a role model for his/her colleagues in terms of teaching, and have the necessary leadership and management skills to move the school forward and improve the quality of pupils' learning in science. The assumption, within the TTA framework, is that subject leaders will have a good grasp of their subject: a sound knowledge and understanding of science and how it can be taught. In some situations the subject leader may be expected to be a specialist teacher, teaching science to other classes throughout the school, although this is still unusual in primary schools. The reality, currently, as we will explore below is a situation where many science co-ordinators get the job because they are enthusiastic, or have generic skills, not because they are 'good' at science.

Subject Leadership in Science – the National Framework

According to the TTA, the core purpose of subject leadership is *to provide profes-sional leadership for a subject to secure high quality teaching and effective use of resources, and to ensure improved standards of achievements for all pupils* (TTA, 1997, p 3). The science subject leader (SSL) is expected to make a significant contribution to school improvement. The effectiveness of the SSL should, according to the TTA, be evident through the sustained improvement of all pupils in their science knowl-edge, understanding and skills in relation to prior attainment. Other indicators of a successful SSL will include a school staff who work together as a team, who are enthusiastic about science and understand its important contribution to pupils' learning. They will have high expectations but set realistic targets; they will be committed to their own on-going professional development.

The National Framework outlines the professional knowledge and understanding (part subject-specific and part generic) that SSLs should have, about:

i. the statutory requirements in science (including assessment, recording and reporting)
ii. the relationship of science to the whole curriculum
iii. the characteristics of high quality teaching in science and strategies for improv-ing standards
iv. relevant research and inspection evidence and pupil achievement data in science
v. the contribution science can make to the development of literacy, numeracy and IT skills
vi. the implications of the Code of Practice for Special Educational Needs for teaching and learning science
vii. health and safety requirements in science.

SSLs need management and administrative skills, attributes and professional competences to lead and manage people to work as individuals and as a team towards a common goal. These attributes include self-confidence, adaptability, energy and perseverance, reliability, enthusiasm for science and integrity. They need the ability to solve problems and have a range of decision-making skills. Communication is a vital aspect of the role, as is self-management: the ability to plan time efficiently and organise oneself well.

The key areas of subject leadership (based on the TTA National Framework) are illustrated in Fig 4.1A.

A. Strategic Direction and Development of Subject
i   develop policy and practices
ii.   create climate of positive attitudes to the subject and confidence in teaching it
iii. establish understanding of importance and role of the subject
iv. analyse and interpret relevant national, local and school data, plus research and inspection evidence
v.   establish, with relevant staff, short-, medium- and long-term plans for developing and resourcing the subject
vi. monitor progress made in achieving subject plans and targets and evaluate effects on teaching and learning to inform future plans

B. Teaching and Learning
i.   ensure curriculum coverage and progression for all pupils
ii.   ensure teachers are clear about objectives and sequence and communicate these to pupils
iii. provide guidance on teaching and learning methods
iv. ensure effective development of literacy, numeracy and IT skills through the subject
v.   establish and implement policies and practices for assessment, recording and reporting ensure records from previous classes and schools used to secure progress
vii. set expectations for staff and pupils in relation to standards of pupil achievement and quality of teaching, establish targets and evaluate progress and achievement in the subject
viii. evaluate teaching and use analysis to inform effective practice and areas of improvement, and take action to improve further quality of teaching
ix. establish a partnership with parents to involve them in their child's learning
x.   develop effective links with the community

C. Leading and Managing Staff
i.   help staff achieve constructive working relationships with pupils
ii.   establish clear expectations and constructive working relationships among staff
iii. sustain motivations and those of other staff
iv. appraise staff (as required by school policy)
v.   audit training needs of staff
vi. lead professional development, e.g. coaching and support, and co-ordinate provision of high-quality professional development
vii. assist teachers to achieve expertise in their subject teaching
viii. work with the SENCO to ensure IEPs are used to set subject-specific targets
ix. ensure headteacher and governors are well informed about policies, plans and priorities and success in meeting objectives, targets and plans

D. Effective and Efficient Deployment of Staff and Resources
i.   establish staff and resource needs for the subject and advise the headteacher
ii.   deploy and advise the headteacher on the deployment of staff
iii. ensure the effective and efficient management and organisation of learning resources, including IT
iv. maintain existing resources and explore opportunities to develop and incorporate new resources
v.   use accommodation to create an effective and stimulating environment for the teaching and learning of the subject
vi. ensure that there is a safe working and learning environment

Fig 4.1A TTA framework for subject leaders 1997

Fundamentally, a leadership role involves *the process of influencing the activities of an organised group towards goal achievement* (Rauch and Belling, 1984). An effective leader shows concern for both people and tasks. It is about establishing sound professional relationships in order to get things done. In words of the Chinese sage Lao Tzu:

> *The best sort of leader is hardly noticed by people. When he [sic] has finished his work, people say, 'We did it ourselves'.*

The science subject leader who can meet all of these requirements and deliver in all the areas outlined is, in the present climate, a rare professional. However, the framework indicates a consensus view that builds on the existing literature in the area (Biggs, 1997; O' Neill and Kitson, 1996; Waters, 1996; Webb and Vulliamy, 1996). It provides a vision of where we might like to get. The next section explores the reality of the current situation, before we consider practical ways forward to better subject leadership.

Current Situation

Recent research (Ritchie, 1997) gives some insights into how teachers become co-ordinators and how they see their role. Of a sample of nearly 100 co-ordinators (spread over 6 LEAs), with at least three years' teaching experience, approximately a third had formally applied for the co-ordinators' roles which they held, others were offered it, were asked, or volunteered to take on the job. Of those who did apply, over half were already working in the school. Less than half the respondents were interviewed for the co-ordination post they then held and less than a third of the posts were reported to be advertised (internally or externally). The vast majority had the role 'permanently' and a salary increase was involved on taking up the role for just over a third. Less than half of the respondents had any specific subject 'qualifications' for the role (i.e. a formal science qualification post-16 or a specialism in science during their initial training). There was little evidence of any formal induction or training for role. Most had, after their appointment, been given opportunities to attend INSET related to their subject (provided by LEAs or Higher Education Institutions (HEIs)) but few had had any INSET specifically related to the work of the co-ordinator. A large number (86%) had a job description (a considerable improvement on the 20% that Bell (1992, p 166) found in his study of science co-ordinators a few years ago) and more than half of these were negotiated. However, problems were evident in terms of the extent to which these are 'realistic' or clarify the different responsibilities (such as for developing a SoW or monitoring pupil attainment) and roles involved (advising, supporting, managing, etc.).

The respondents were asked to indicate which of the following tasks they were expected to carry out and how often, which were their priorities and which did they rate as important:

a) Write or review a school policy
b) Produce or modify a scheme of work
c) Make decisions about purchasing items
d) Be responsible for equipment and materials

e) Organise staff meetings
f) Talk to parents about the subject
g) Talk to governors about the subject
h) Liaise with a feeder school(s)
i) Liaise with schools their pupils go on to
j) Offer colleagues advice
k) Support colleagues in their classrooms
l) Monitor teachers' plans
m) Monitor classroom learning
n) Deal with concerns related to pupils with SEN
o) Teach the subject to children in other classes
p) Deal with assessment, recording and reporting
q) Organise school-based in-service activities
r) Produce resources for colleagues to use.

Fig 4.1B illustrates some of the results.

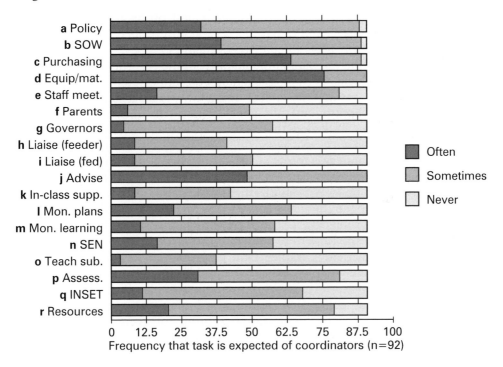

Fig 4.1B

The data showed that tasks related to resources (c and d) were those carried out most frequently. Providing advice for colleagues (j), work on policies and on whole-school Schemes of Work (SoW) (a and b) were regularly expected of co-ordinators. It was not surprisingly, in the light of national assessment and OFSTED require-ments, to find assessment issues (p) and monitoring (l and m) quite high on the list. Monitoring of teachers plans (l) was more frequently done than the monitoring of children's learning (m). This is possibly because the latter was perceived to be more difficult without non-contact time, although increasingly co-ordinators are monitoring samples of children's work. The monitoring of plans has also been common in the past (although previously more often done by head teachers). The tasks least often expected of co-ordinators were teaching the science to children in other classes (o) and supporting colleagues in their classrooms (k). Clearly, the encouragement for more specialist subject teaching in primary schools (Alexander *et al*, 1992) has had little impact on practice in the schools sampled.

There was congruence between co-ordinators' priorities, their rating of the importance of tasks and what they were expected to do. For example, a very high priority was being given to SoW. In the early nineties, Bell (1992) found policy development was regarded as a higher priority. It can be assumed that most schools now have policies and the focus is on how that policy can be implemented through SoW (which are also necessary to provide OFSTED inspectors with evidence that statutory requirements are being met). There was evidence, however, that co-ordinators would like to be given more opportunities to work in other teachers classrooms (k) as a means of providing support and professional development. Liaison with other schools (h and i), parents (f) and governors (g) were tasks given low priority and apparently less valued by co-ordinators.

A picture emerged from the data of the majority of the co-ordinators feeling well supported by their headteachers and reasonably well supported by their colleagues. Headteachers' support was described most frequently as moral support, or in terms of financial/resource support and non-contact time (the latter being the most valued). OFSTED have indicated that *science co-ordinators need sufficient non-teaching time to develop their role more fully, including the monitoring of science teaching* (1995, p 5). About two thirds of the sample had non-contact time (associated with their co-ordination role). The average of all those given non-contact time was approximately 2.75 hours per month (the sample of schools involved an average size of 9 teachers), although there was considerable variation, for example a temporary increase when the subject is a School Development Plan (SDP) priority area. Issues about the use of the time were evident: in some cases the time was used for general class–teacher activities, rather than co-ordination activities; in the best examples, use of the time was planned and focused on specific tasks; in a few cases there were established teacher release systems in the schools which allowed co-ordinators to work alongside colleagues on a regular basis, in one school there was a written policy about the use of this time; few co-ordinators were using the time for systematic monitoring in classrooms (confirming OFSTED findings (1994, p 90)). It was more common for time to be spent on resources, writing SoW or monitoring teachers' plans, SAT results and children's work. There was little evidence of use of non-contact time being monitored or evaluated.

Another key aspect of support for co-ordinators concerns the finances available and whether they are given responsibility for purchasing. According to the data collected, less than two-thirds were given a budget to spend on resources and equipment. The amount varied enormously and was often linked to the School Development Plan (SDP). The average (of those with control of a budget) was about £350. A majority of those that did not have a budget wanted one, or at least more information regarding the allocation of finances. Reference was made to the difficulty of long-term planning without knowledge of the finances available.

In terms of support from outside school, the situation was not very positive. Many referred to the valuable support they gained from cluster meetings that were facilitated by LEA staff (in the past). It seems that few cluster groups have survived the reduction in LEA support. Only a small minority belonged to a professional association, such as the ASE.

It is hardly surprising that the overwhelming majority of respondents considered that there were constraints on them in terms of their co-ordinators' work. Webb and Vulliamy (1996, p 91), in their study of 50 schools, identified three main factors constraining the role: co-ordinator expertise, lack of time and power relations within the school. These emerged in the data under discussion, but with different emphases. Insufficient time (especially non-contact) to do the job was an almost unanimous factor (many referred to amount of time that they spent outside school hours on co-ordinator tasks). There was frequent reference to the lack of opportunities to get into other classrooms (for support and monitoring purposes). Too much paperwork was a comment associated with lack of time from some respondents. The tension between their teaching and co-ordination role was a concern for many, again linked to the issue of having time to do all expected of them. This issue was particularly problematic for Y2 and Y6 teachers, with their additional assessment burden. There were very few respondents who had responsibility for just one area of the curriculum and balancing the different areas of responsibility was recognised as difficult. Teachers in small schools were suffering most in this respect. There was evidence that core subject responsibilities were being prioritised over foundation subject responsibilities. Insufficient money for equipment and resources was the second constraint most regularly mentioned. Other constraints that were often highlighted concerned co-ordinators' expertise, including, their lack of experience of other Key Stages (in primary schools) and their (perceived) lack of subject knowledge.

Despite all of the constraints mentioned, there was also a picture of many co-ordinators enjoying their role (supporting findings from Bell's earlier study (1996, p.11) and wanting to do more, if they only had the opportunities.

Challenges Facing Co-ordinators as They Develop into Subject Leaders

OFSTED (1996) set an agenda for schools to address what they described as 'the current unsatisfactory situation' with regard to subject co-ordination. They asked schools to consider how co-ordinators may:

i) *develop their role as managers for their subject;*

ii) *have opportunities to influence policy and planning, to monitor and guide teaching, and to oversee resource provision;*

iii) *have, maintain, or acquire adequate specialist knowledge to make them effective and confident in their role;*

iv) *have sufficient time to carry out these responsibilities;*

v) *have access to the necessary inservice training and contacts, and opportunities to lead subject training for colleagues.*

There are some daunting challenges for co-ordinators, seeking to develop their role as subject leaders, some of which are discussed below. This Guide, and in particular the chapters that follow, are intended to support you (if you are a co-ordinator) in meeting these challenges.

The first challenge is to make opportunities for tackling your responsibilities and, if you are lucky enough, making the most of non-contact time. There are no simple answers here, but experience suggests a lot can be achieved by careful prioritising and time-management – be realistic about what you can achieve and do what you set out to do as well as you can.

Schools are communities with their own distinct cultures (Day *et al*, 1993). The SSL is, in effect, an agent of change. To be successful in this role requires the SSL to understand the culture in which he/she works and establish the professional relationships that are conducive to change. These relationships, with the headteacher and colleagues, and the creation of a collaborative culture, are, perhaps, the key challenge for science subject leaders (Bell and Ritchie, 1998). A sometimes neglected dimension of the professional development needs of SLs is 'the management of change' – there is much we can all learn about this process and how best to facilitate it (Fullan, 1991; West, 1995). In the context of thinking about encouraging change, it is worth reflecting on whether there may be disadvantages in placing too much emphasis on 'the role' as opposed to specific tasks. If colleagues assume that the SSL will take full responsibility for the development of science it may be assumed that no one else has to. A more constructive approach may be to work towards a 'task culture' (West, 1996) in which the SSL works with groups of colleagues, or the whole staff, on specific tasks, identified through school development planning.

Another important challenge for a new co-ordinator is to find out 'where the school is' in terms of science. Carrying out an audit (see Chapter 4.2) of the current situation is a necessary prerequisite to planning for the future and setting realistic targets. There are many aspects of science which can be audited: teaching styles, colleagues' strengths and weaknesses, resources, budgets, approaches to planning in science, pupils' achievements and/or experiences of science, etc. It is best to collect information from a variety of sources, to ensure that decisions about future action based on evidence rather than impression. An audit will help the SSL set long- (3–5 years), medium- (6–12 months) and short-term (next few weeks) goals, which should be aimed at improving quality and standards in science. Of course, ideally, such action planning will be collaborative and set in the context of the whole school development plan (SDP). When setting targets and planning action, it is worth considering 'maintenance tasks' and 'developmental tasks' (both of which should be included in a SDP and have a budget). As a SSL there will need to be a balance between these (for example, a maintenance task may involve reordering consumable items on a regular basis, a developmental task may be to introduce Nuffield Primary Science materials throughout Key Stage 1 (over the next 3 years), with appropriate staff development). Developmental tasks are usually harder, but maintenance tasks can be reassuring in that they can usually be done fairly quickly and give you a sense of achieving something!

In a climate where the political imperative is clearly focused on literacy and numeracy there is a continuing need to ensure that science is valued and is given adequate time and attention by colleagues. There is still a 'selling job' to be done in many schools. An audit may help identify the extent to which this is an issue in a particular school.

Auditing has much in common with on-going monitoring and evaluation (about which you can read more in Chapter 4.2). Monitoring teaching and learning, which in many small primary schools will be a responsibility shared with the headteacher, is a challenge which will be relatively new to many SSLs, although informal monitoring has always be a feature of good practice in science co-ordination. In the context of OFSTED inspections and the focus on standards of pupil achievement in science, this task could be argued to be the key area in which SSLs will need to develop their expertise over the next few years.

Professional development in the area of science will remain a priority for several years: there remain too many colleagues who, even after years of national funding for 20, 10 and 5-day science courses (which finally ends in 1997/98), and other LEA and HEI provided INSET, have still not had adequate in-service support. The role of LEA advisers and inspectors has also been changing over the last few years (with more emphasis on monitoring and inspection than advice). Consequently SSLs need to give careful consideration to identifying the staff development needs of colleagues (as well as their own) and planning how to meet those needs. In some cases the support may well be best provided in school by the SSL, perhaps organising workshops or providing in-class support (see Ollerenshaw and Ritchie, 1997, and Chapter 8), in others, organising support from outside the school or attending externally provided courses may be preferable. Increasingly, materials are being developed to support SSLs in this aspect of their work (OU, 1996).

The school community exists within a wider community and the SSL has a part to play in improving relations with parents, other schools (from which pupils come, or to which they progress) and the local community. Such relationships can have an undeniable benefit on children's learning. Encouraging parents to become more involved in their children's learning in science, in the way that many already are in terms of English and mathematics is worth considering as a priority which may have other unexpected benefits for science and its profile in school. Gaining support of governors and others for science can also provide surprises in terms of what may be offered: untapped enthusiasms, expertise, generosity, etc.

For many SSLs, preparing for an OFSTED inspection may seem like the biggest challenge they face. However, as Chapter 4.4 illustrates, the process can be developmental and focus the school on key issues that need addressing if pupils are to receive the science education they deserve – and as we know, they only get one chance.

Conclusion

If science is to continue to be regarded as a 'success story' as we go into the next millenium, then science co-ordinators will need to meet these challenges, building on progress made over recent years, and recognising the new demands a science subject leadership role implies. The nature of the science curriculum that will be taught after the turn of the century is, at the time of writing, still uncertain.

However, what is clear is the importance of the contribution that teachers should be making to the debate and consultation about that new science curriculum. Science subject leaders should be ensuring those voices are heard, through school discussions, at LEA meetings, within the ASE and in other professional contexts. The current science curriculum is not a 'right answer' and there are alternatives to be proposed. Science has a vital part to play in the education of all children – we must ensure that the science we teach is relevant, accessible and appropriate. Let's continue to 'make it work'.

About the Author

Ron Ritchie is Head of Department for Professional Development at Bath Spa University College. Before working in higher education, he taught in primary schools and was an advisory teacher for primary science in the then Avon LEA. He is co-author with the late Chris Ollerenshaw, of *Primary Science: Making It Work* which is published by David Fulton.

References and Further Reading

Alexander, R., Rose, J. and Woodhead, C. (1992) *Curriculum Organisation and Classroom Practice in Primary Schools: a Discussion Paper*. London: DES.

Bell, D. (1992) *Coordinating Science in Primary Schools: a Role Model?* Evaluation and Research in Education. Vol 6, Nos 2 and 3, pp 155–171.

Bell, D. (1996) *Subject Specialist, Co-ordinator, Leader or Manager?* Unpublished paper presented at BERA Conference, Lancaster University.

Bell, D. and Ritchie, R. (1998) *From Subject Co-ordinator to Subject Leader*. Open University Press.

Biggs, M. (1997) *Your Role as a Primary School Subject Co-ordinator*. London, Hodder and Stoughton.

Day, C., Hall, C., Gammage, P. and Coles, M. (1993) *Leadership and Curriculum in the Primary School*. London, Paul Chapman Publishing Ltd.

Department of Education and Science (DES) (1993). *Curriculum Organisation and Classroom Practice in Primary Schools: a follow-up report*. London, HMSO.

Department for Education and Employment (DfEE) (1997) *Excellence in Education (White Paper)*. London: DfEE.

Fullan, M. (1991) *The New Meaning of Educational Change (2nd Edition)*. London, Cassell.

OFSTED (1994) *Primary Matters*. London, HMSO.

OFSTED (1995) *Science: a review of inspection findings 1993/94*. London, HMSO.

OFSTED (1996) *Subjects and Standards*. London, HMSO.

Ollerenshaw, C. and Ritchie, R. (1997) *Primary Science: Making it Work (2nd Edition)*. London, David Fulton Publishers.

O'Neill, J. and Kitson, N. (Eds) (1996) *Effective Curriculum Management*. London, Routledge.

Open University (1996) *Primary Teachers Learning Science. (S624).* Milton Keynes, Open University Press.

Rauch, C. and Behling, O. (1984) Functionalism. In Hunt, J. (Ed) *Leaders and Managers.* New York, Pergamon.

Ritchie, R. (1997) *The subject coordinator's role and responsibilities in primary schools.* Proceedings of the 3rd Primary Science Conference, Durham University, July.

Teacher Training Agency (TTA) (1997) *National Standards for Subject Leaders.* London, TTA.

Waters, M. (1996) *Curriculum Co-ordinators in Primary Schools.* London, Collins Educational.

Webb, R. and Vulliamy, G. (1996) *Roles and Responsibilities in the Primary School.* Buckingham, Open University Press.

West, N. (1995) *Middle Management in the Primary School.* London, David Fulton Publishers.

West, N. (1996) *Subject Coordinators: They can't make it alone.* Managing Schools Today, March, pp 18–20.

4.2 Reviewing and Monitoring Science

Jane Bourne

An interesting development over the last year has been to redefine the role of the subject co-ordinator. The TTA has set out standards for subject leaders in the document National Standards For Subject Leaders which was published in July 1997. Within this framework the role of the subject leader has been defined in five areas. In section one, on the core purpose of subject leadership, the TTA suggests that the subject leaders role in reviewing and monitoring science in the school should:

> ...evaluate the effectiveness of teaching and learning, the subject curriculum and progress towards targets for pupils and staff to inform future priorities and targets for the subject. The degree to which a subject leader is involved in monitoring to provide the range of information for evaluation will depend on school policy and be influenced by the size of the school. Although the subject leader will undertake a variety of monitoring activities, the Headteacher in smaller primary schools may retain a larger proportion of that monitoring which requires direct classroom observation of teaching and learning.

In this chapter it is intended to look at how the subject leader may be involved in reviewing and monitoring science within their school. The TTA has conceded that all schools are different and the monitoring role of a subject leader in a three-teacher school will be very different from that of a teacher in a 20-teacher urban primary school. (See Chapter 4.1.)

Monitoring and Evaluating

Like continuity and progression these terms are becoming a part of everyday education speak. It is necessary to define what the authors mean by each term.

Monitoring is the collection of information about a specific aspect of the schools performance.

Evaluation is the making of judgements about the quality of performance based on the information gathered.

But what does this look like in practise? Each area can be broken down into smaller steps. For the purposes of this chapter three steps will be considered:

INPUT FACTORS	⇨	PROCESS FACTORS	⇨	OUTPUT FACTORS
Scheme of work Teacher plans		Lesson observation		Pupils' views Pupils' work Test results

Monitoring Input Factors

Input factors are perhaps the easiest to monitor. After the scheme of work has been produced, the effectiveness of this scheme in promoting effective teaching and learning will need to be addressed. Many schools have schemes of work that have been running for a couple of years and therefore due for review (here a scheme of work is defined as the subject policy, long- and medium-term planning). (See Chapter 3.1.)

As a subject leader a few questions need to be asked.

- Does the long-term plan allow for visiting areas of Sc1, 2, 3 and 4 every year?
- Is it sequenced in a way that allows areas of the programmes of study to be revisited in a different context thus allowing for progression?
- Does medium-term planning identify what ideas the children are likely to have in this area already?
- Does it give clear guidance to colleagues on how concepts can be taught effectively and how this can be followed by tasks in which pupils can demonstrate understanding by applying ideas in investigations and other practical activities?
- Does the work provide opportunities for a recorded assessment of achievement?
- Is the scheme linked to the broader school aims?
- Does the medium-term plan provide the opportunity to progress in each year in the major concept areas? This may mean splitting up units of work that have traditionally been taught together, and recombining and sequencing units within a key stage.
- Does each topic area have an agreed set of learning outcomes defined so that colleagues can use for setting work at an appropriate level and also for assessment purposes?
- Is the time allocated to an area sensible, e.g. a 10 week topic on electricity in year three would clearly not be sensible.
- Does the medium-term plan give clear guidance on how differentiation is to be achieved? If using learning outcomes that are linked to levels, are they used to set work for different groups of children at an appropriate level, or for assessment purposes (differentiation by outcome) or a mixture of both?
- Do colleagues find the medium-term plans easy to use? Are they too detailed and therefore provide a straight jacket rather than a framework?

Using this framework of questions the subject leader can begin to appraise where planning is good and where improvements can be made. It is a good idea to question other colleagues to elicit their views on the implementation of the plans and their ease of use.

Some subject leaders will do this on a termly basis by collecting in copies of class lists with outcomes for each pupil clearly marked off. In the case cited below outcomes are written at three levels and the co-ordinator checks them to see the profile of the class. If he/she finds that all pupils have attained the highest outcomes for the unit of work, it means one of two things, i.e. the unit has been well taught and very well understood by all the pupils or, the outcomes have been set at a too low level. This is a very quick method of checking for the subject leader which also provides an overview of attainment when the class teacher comes to write reports. An example of this is shown in Fig 4.2A.

LEARNING OUTCOMES   Unit _____ Body Maintenance/Sex Ed   year 6

Differentiated Learning Outcomes   TAGS

BASIC LEVEL

A	Label a simple diagram of the heart with the appropriate vocabulary given.
B	Be able to know 5 different types of exercise
C	Know that the blood circulates around the body
D	Know that exercise affects the heart and pulse. Be able to find the heart.
E	

STANDARD LEVEL

F	Label a simple diagram of the heart.
G	Classify different types of exercise, eg vigorous, steady, quick burst.
H	Show on a simple diagram of the circulatory system which way the blood circulates around the body.
I	Measure changes in heart and pulse rate before and after exercise.
J	State that during exercise more blood is needed by the muscles.

EXTENSION LEVEL

K	To draw and label a simple diagram of the heart.
L	Give 5 positive effects of exercise on the body.
M	To draw a simple diagram of the circulatory system showing which way the blood circulates around the body.
N	State that blood carries oxygen to the muscles in the body and carries carbon dioxide away.
O	

RECORD SHEET
Unit Body Maintenance
Yr 6 _____

Learning Outcomes and tags

Names	A	B	C	D	E	F	G	H	I	J	K	L	M	N	O
Anna	✓	✓	✓	✓		✓	✓								
Barry	✓	✓	✓	✓			✓								
Claire	✓	✓	✓	✓											
David	✓	✓	✓	✓											
Edward															
Freddy	✓	✓	✓	✓		✓	✓	✓	✓	✓	✓	✓	✓	✓	
Garry	✓	✓	✓	✓		✓	✓	✓	✓	✓	✓	✓	✓		
Harriet	✓	✓	✓	✓		✓	✓	✓	✓	✓	✓	✓			
Imran	✓	✓	✓	✓		✓	✓	✓	✓	✓					
Karen	✓	✓	✓	✓		✓	✓	✓	✓	✓	✓	✓	✓	✓	
Liam	✓	✓	✓	✓		✓	✓	✓	✓	✓	✓	✓	✓	✓	
Martin	✓	✓	✓	✓		✓	✓	✓	✓	✓	✓	✓	✓	✓	
Norman	✓	✓	✓	✓		✓	✓	✓	✓	✓	✓	✓	✓	✓	
Olive	✓	✓	✓	✓		✓	✓	✓	✓	✓	✓		✓	✓	
Peter	✓	✓	✓	✓		✓	✓	✓	✓	✓	✓	✓	✓	✓	

Fig 4.2A

It can be seen from the example in Fig 4.2A that Anna, Barry, Claire, and David are all operating at 'basic' level. In this school basic level is equated to National Curriculum level 3 in year 5 and 6 ('standard' is level 4 and 'extension' level 5). Edward has missed the whole unit of work. Freddy works with Garry, Imran, and Jane but is clearly achieving a higher level of attainment. The other group of pupils, Karen to Peter, all have a very clear understanding of this work. This school has the outcomes for Sc1 on a separate sheet to enable them to track skills development. When the subject leader receives a copy of this sheet termly or half termly, dependant on the length of the topic, he/ she is able to very quickly monitor that the unit of work has been taught and to what extent different groups of pupils have understood the different concepts.

If reference is also made to the individual teachers' plans it can be determined whether groups of children have not been taught the higher level concepts or have had access to them but not understood them.

When these outcomes sheets are viewed at the end of a year it becomes apparent where misunderstandings have occurred and then next year's plans are adjusted accordingly. Where a school works on a two-year rolling programme the cycle for review is obviously longer.

Monitoring Output Factors

In this section we will consider three output factors; pupils work, their views and test results.

It is a good idea to sample pupils' work periodically. Ask colleagues to supply you with a sample of higher-, middle- and lower-attaining pupils work. Just two or three examples will be sufficient. You will look at the work with a number of questions to be answered.

- Has the scheme of work for that topic been followed?
- Has the work been marked in accordance with school marking policy and comments given to show pupils how to improve?
- Is the work of each group of pupils set at an appropriate level? Are the pupils able to extend their knowledge and skills if they have achieved the lower targets?
- Is there a good balance between investigational work and teacher-directed activities?

Having sampled the work in this way a good idea of how well the pupils are achieving can be gained. If when the sample of Year 3 work is looked at and you find that all children are attaining level 2 but none is attaining level 3, then clearly a discussion with the class teacher is needed. Perhaps this is a particularly low-attaining group of pupils or maybe the teacher's own knowledge of a particular concept is not sufficiently developed to have the confidence to take the pupils further. In the later case, there is a need to provide some in school in-service training, in the short term, and perhaps some help from an outside agency in the longer term.

As a result of work sampling, a few examples should be kept to create, or add to, a portfolio of assessed work. This portfolio should represent the levels awarded in each of the strands of the National Curriculum. These levels should be agreed by all members of staff and therefore provide a benchmark of the standards expected in the school. Agreeing standards for pieces of work is not new but some teachers still feel uncomfortable about levelling pieces of work of their pupils. If this is the case the SCAA booklet *Exemplification of Standards* (1995) is a good source of anonymous pieces of work which has the advantage of providing the answers! This booklet can be used as a starter and is much less threatening for some teachers. A portfolio such as this can be invaluable for new members of staff entering the school to gauge the standards expected there.

Talking with pupils is another good way of finding out what they know, understand and enjoy about their science lessons. This does not need to be a formal interview, it could just be a chat in the playground or asking them to tell you about a piece of work that they have on display. Sharing assemblies are another way of not only engaging the interest of the pupils but for all members of staff to see the standards of work achieved in other classes and year groups.

More recent developments in monitoring require the analysis of test data. Teacher assessments at the end of key stage 1 and test results at the end of key stage 2 can be used as an indicator of performance. Careful use of this data can provide an insight into trends in year groups. It is worth remembering that for any meaningful analysis of test data the number of pupils in the year group should be 20 or more, any fewer and the reliability of the data can be doubtful. The two tables in Fig 4.2B are the results for a moderate sized primary school with two classes per year group of about 28 pupils in each. The tables indicate the percentage of pupils attaining each level.

The tables present rather a daunting set of figures on first glance, but if you take each column and compare across, a few details begin to emerge.

Firstly at Key Stage 1:

• Why is there a lack of level 3s? Is this group of children particularly poor or is there a lack of confidence in the Year 2 teachers in awarding level 3?
• There are more boys awarded level 2 than girls. If the year group size was 56 this would mean that the difference in percentage terms equates to 4.5. pupils. You may judge that this is not a significant difference and therefore would not be too worried by the figures.

Key Stage 2 presents other challenges. If the first two columns are compared it would appear that the school is underestimating the achievement of boys. If then you compare those to the next column it can be seen that the test results also indicate a higher achievement than the teacher assessment shows. When compared to the national test scores, there is a lack of achievement at the higher levels.

If we now compare the girls and national teacher assessments again there appears to be an underestimate of performance. As this is now an issue for both sexes (as can be seen in the final columns) teacher assessment could be an area that needs future development. There also appears to be significant under-assessment of boys' performance when compared with that of the girls.

The 12% difference in test scores at level 5 in this year group of 60 represents 7 pupils; again it is up to the school to decide if this a measure of under-performance. When some analysis of the figures has taken place questions will undoubtedly have been raised. All the figures can do is raise the questions, it is then up to the subject

Key Stage 1

	School Boys TA	National Boys TA	School Girls TA	National Girls TA	School Boy/Girl	National Boy/Girl
W	0	2	0	2	0	4
1	25	28	33	30	28	29
2	75	53	67	51	72	50
3	0	17	0	17	0	17

Key Stage 2

	SB TA	NB TA	SB TT	NB TT	SG TA	NG TA	SG TT	NG TT	S BG TA	N BG TA	S BG TT	N BG TT
W	0	0	0	0	0	0	0	0	0	0	0	0
1	5	1	0	0	0	0	0	0	2.5	1	0	0
2	20	7	15	4	10	6	15	4	15	6	15	4
3	60	28	27	17	70	29	28	20	65	29	27.5	19
4	15	48	48	47	20	51	47	48	17.5	50	47.5	48
5	0	15	10	24	0	13	10	20	0	14	10	22
6	0	0	0	0	0	0	0	0	0	0	0	0

Key:

SBTA   School boys teacher assessment
NBTA   National boys teacher assessment
SGTA   School girls teacher assessment
NGTA   National girls teacher assessment
TT   Test and Task
BG   Boy girl.

Fig 4.2B Results at Key Stage 1 and Key Stage 2

leader in consultation with the head to provide some answers. Often there will not be straight forward answers, it will depend very much on the nature and make up of the different year groups (more of this later). As more data becomes available, year on year, trends and patterns can be sought. It would be folly to attempt to make any major changes based on just one year's figures.

Monitoring Process Factors

This is the most difficult area to monitor. Teachers are not trained as OFSTED inspectors in the art of classroom observation and often find this part of the role the most threatening. For these reasons, monitoring the process comes after all the other forms of monitoring have taken place.

There must be a very clearly defined reason for visiting a colleague's lesson. Just popping in to have a look is not good enough. In order to build trust it is a good idea to invite a colleague to look at your lesson first. Have a check list available so that the focus for the visit is defined. It might be that you want them to look at the way in which you set up an open-ended investigation for the whole class, which is differentiated by outcome, and you want your colleague to look at the time you spend with each group of pupils. Allow time before the lesson to discuss what you will be doing and then time at the end for feedback. If you are given time to monitor using classroom observation make sure that there is an agreed focus for the visit. There is nothing more frustrating than receiving feedback on an element of a lesson that was not to be the focus of the observation. It is a good idea to take notes so that you remember the elements of a lesson that you want to feed back on, but it is not a good idea to carry a clip board and distance yourself from the lesson totally. The pupils find this odd behaviour off-putting. It should be made clear that you are observing lessons to look at pupils' attainment not to judge the quality of teaching. Often the teacher you are looking at will be monitoring your performance in another subject area!

The time to do any sort of monitoring needs to be provided. There are a number of ways of making small amounts of time available. These can be used effectively for different kinds of monitoring. The table in Fig 4.2C below shows the most common ways of creating time for monitoring to take place.

Model	Description	Input Factors	Process Factors	Output Factors	Advantages	Disadvantages
1	Head / deputy release time	✓	✓	✓		
2	Team teaching to release a colleague	✓	✓	✓		
3	Use of non contact time	✓	✓	✓		
4	Use of supply teacher	✓	✓	✓		
5	Use of directed time	✓		✓		
6	Use of advisory teacher support	✓		✓		
7	Release from whole school activities – assemblies	✓		✓		
8	Use of own time.					

Fig 4.2C Creating time

Obviously it is harder to create time to monitor the process than it is to monitor input and output factors, as this can be a fairly solitary occupation. Models 3 and 4 have financial implications which may prove prohibitory. The amount of non-contact time in primary schools is negligible and probably not an option. The advantages and disadvantages of each model will vary depending on the size of schools. The use of own time should not really be an option if monitoring is to be successful.

To help with the evaluation role after all the evidence has been collected, the production of a subject development plan should be drawn up. This of course will fit in with the school development plan and define in more detail the developments which will take place in science over the next 12 to 18 months.

A useful pro-forma for the production of a subject development plan can be found in the ASE publication *Primary Self Review Document* (ASE,1997).

A subject development plan should outline:

- what needs to be done in priority order
- how this will be achieved and by whom
- what spending implications this has
- what the success criteria are
- time scales.

This plan should be looked at each term in order to see which areas have been met and which still need further work.

The Subject Leader's Role in Target Setting

The new requirement set out in the White Paper, *Excellence in Schools*, for schools to set targets for themselves based on benchmark data has clear implications for the subject leader's role in monitoring.

The White paper states:

> *From September 1998, each school will be required to have challenging targets for improvement. If schools are to take their targets seriously, it is important that they should take direct responsibility for them.*
>
> *School targets should be based on:*
>
> - *benchmark information on the performance of similar schools, at national and local level;*
> - *information on the rate of progress needed to achieve national targets and*
> - *the most recent inspection evidence.*

The idea of setting targets for individual pupils and to some extent the setting of targets to improve for schools performance is not new. However the setting of these targets against a benchmark is. Let us define the difference between a target and a benchmark as they mean something quite different from each other.

Benchmark information is based on the performance of groups of schools with similar characteristics and may be calculated in a number of ways. National benchmarks are set using Form 7 data on the number of pupils who took a free school lunch on the day the form was completed. Locally, benchmarks can be made using test scores which are collated by an LEA. This would usually be based on reading scores obtained by pupils taking a nationally standardised test. (See Chapter 3.2.)

Having gained information from two sources, a school may well find that it is in two different benchmark groups. Each benchmark information will place it in a group together with the scores of the rest of the schools in that group, stating where the top, middle and bottom quartile scores for the group lie.

If we take a fictitious primary school, East Town CP, and look at what a bench mark might look like it will then be possible to set targets based on the bench marks.

School roll

Year	No
1995	275
1996	265
1997	257

School staffing

Year	No
1996	15.4
1997	15.4

Free school meals

Year	% of roll	LEA average
1995	15	15
1996	15	15
1997	14	16

% of roll registered SEN 1997 = 1.37

Key Stage 2 test results. Percentage of pupils at or above levels 4 or 5.

1996

	Level 4 or above			Level 5 or above		
Pupils 66	School	LEA	National	School	LEA	National
English	57	49	48	6	7	7
Mathematics	48	42	44	8	9	12
Science	79	72	70	28	23	22

1997

	Level 4 or above			Level 5 or above		
Pupils 67	School	LEA	National	School	LEA	National
English	49	58	56	6	11	12
Mathematics	44	54	53	9	12	14
Science	63	65	61	9	15	14

Fig 4.2D School data sheet for East Town CP

East Town was placed in a group of schools which had a mean 8+ reading score of between 98 and 100. The data for the other schools in the group, based on Key Stage 2 test scores of those attaining level 4 or above, are shown in Fig 4.2E.

	English	Mathematics	Science
Upper quartile (top 25% schools) scored above:	52	51	75
Scores of top school in each group (best overall average)	71	65	75
East Town data taken from the school data sheet	55	56	72

The highest recorded science score was 82.

Fig 4.2E

East town was placed in another benchmark group based on the percentage of free school meals (FSM) data. This group was calculated to include those schools with between 14 and 20% FSM. The data for this group are shown in Fig 4.2F.

	English	Mathematics	Science
Upper quartile (top 25% schools) scored above:	63	59	72
Scores of top school in each group (best overall average)	71	65	75
East Town data taken from the school data sheet	55	56	72

The top science score in this group was 79.

Fig 4.2F

When comparing these two sets of benchmark data, it would be advantageous to use the benchmarks based on free school meals as East Town comes into the top quartile of schools already, LEAs may however decide that schools should use reading test data.

Once a school decision is made, the same benchmark data must be used to set targets across all the core subjects. If we assume that there were 69 pupils in Year 6 in 1997. To reach the highest score in science of the schools in Fig 4.2E (based on reading scores), i.e. from 72% level 4 and above to 82%, then 7 pupils would need to attain level 4 from level 3.

This is when Target Setting comes into play. As subject leader, you may decide that 7 pupils is too many to move forward to level 4 in a year, so you decide to target 4 as a more manageable number. Looking at the figures the school may decide that moving pupils' achievement in maths and English is more of a priority.

A process for setting targets could be summarised as:

- Collect data.
- Decide on which benchmark data to use.
- The highest science score was 82%. In order for me to achieve that score with my year group of 69 pupils I would need to move 7 pupils from level 3 to level 4.
- Looking at the profile of attainment the current Year 6 are exhibiting, I decide if this is too many or not enough.
- Is their attainment similar to last years' Year 6?
- Are there any pupils who are performing similarly to those who attained level 3 last year?
- What can I do to help them attain better scores?
- What can I do to ensure that the level 4s and above maintain their progress?
- What can I do to support the potential level 2 pupils?
(See also Chapter 4.4.)

Only when questions of this type have been answered can realistic targets be set. In order to set realistic targets many factors must be taken into account. Ralf Tabberer writing in the *Education Journal*, December 1996 (Seven Obstacles to Effective Target Setting), talks about setting SMART targets. This has been a term adopted by the DFEE in their publication From Targets to Action (1997). The term SMART stands for:

Specific
Measurable
Achievable
Realistic
Time related

For East Town CP this could be translated to mean:

Specific – 4 pupils achieving level 4 this year who at the moment are projected to achieve level 3.
Measurable – Monitor the progress of these pupils, as defined earlier. Target specific areas for them, e.g. practice at labelling diagrams. Test results will provide the measure.
Achievable – The target is carefully defined to be achievable.
Realistic – In the case of East Town, to target this number of pupils (i.e. 4) is realistic.
Time related – Set a limit to the time in which to prepare the pupils for achieving their targets.

As targets are to be made for a three-year period (in the case of Key Stage 1 this does not mean setting targets for pupils that you have not seen yet) it is worth bearing in mind that targets can go down as well as up. It could be that a particular year group or class has suffered because of a teacher's absence, or their attainment on entry was particularly low. In these cases it is quite acceptable to set a target for that year that is lower than the year before.

To many people the idea of moving pupils up through levels in order to attain a higher benchmark score goes against their way of teaching.There is no suggestion from the author that targets are set for one group of pupils to the exclusion of all the others. The whole idea of monitoring and evaluating is to track the progress of all pupils in the school not just the more able.

If statistics and data are used sensibly they will enable subject leaders and head-teachers to target pupils in groups to receive the support that they need. It will also highlight staff development needs within the school.

About the Author

Jane Bourne is County Advisory Teacher for Science and Environmental Education working for Suffolk LEA. She was a member of the ASE Assessment and Examinations committee for 3 years and has written a number of publications on all phases of science education.

References and Further Reading

TTA (1997) *National Standards for Subject Leaders*. Teacher Training Agency.

SCAA (1995) *Exemplification of Standards*. SCAA.

Department for Education and Employment (DfEE) (1997) *Excellence in Schools*. White Paper. London, DfEE.

Tabberer, R. (1996) *Seven Obstacles to Effective Target Setting*. Education Journal

DfEE (1997) *From Targets to Action*. London, DfEE.

4.3 Resources for Teaching Science

Martin Hollins

High-quality teaching of science is dependent on the availability of high-quality and appropriate resources. (ASE, 1998)

The Association is unequivocal in its policy statement on quality in science education. Similarly, in OFSTED's review of the teaching of science, there is the clear statement that it is the role of the science co-ordinator to manage these resources (OFSTED 1996). This chapter is designed to address the task of identifying, managing and using high quality and appropriate resources. (See Chapter 4.1.)

Introduction

There is a lack of research information on the relationship between resourcing and the quality of teaching, or even on what constitutes adequate resources. Official reports such as OFSTED school inspection reports rarely make these connections. A recent report on secondary science resourcing (Royal Society 1997) strongly suggests that schools are under-funded for resources, and that this is getting worse. Two reasons the report gives for this are the national curriculum requirements for more investigations, and the expansion of ICT, both of which require expensive provision. One could draw the conclusion from this that high-quality science education must include substantial use of investigations and ICT and so the science done on low budgets will not have the same quality. In primary schools, common experience is of tight budgets and 'wish lists', as opposed to resourcing that schools are proud of.

If such constraints are a common feature of schools now and in the future, then the effective management of resources is all the more important, to ensure the best education for children that is possible in the circumstances. In order to achieve the aims and learning outcomes of the previous sections of the guide, it is clear that a wide range of resources is required, including:

- materials and equipment (consumable and non-consumable)
- access to living things to study (including in natural environments)
- visits to museums, etc. and fieldwork outings
- access to other people as sources of expertise
- print resources – publications and school-produced documents
- media resources (including computer-based and educational broadcasts).

This chapter considers the issues involved in choosing and using each of these in turn.

The Management of Resources

The practical organisation of resources will be dependent both on the physical environment of the school and on the nature of the resource. There are, however, a number of common educational issues which the science co-ordinator needs to address.

Planning

In view of the importance of resources to educational quality, and of their budget implications, they need to be included in any curriculum policy development. This should include the following aspects:

- The contribution of resources to achieving educational aims. For example the national curriculum requires that pupils develop their skills in choosing and using science equipment.
- Audit of existing resources held in the school – it is often surprising how much is 'hidden' and unused in cupboards.
- Storage and access – how will the educational aims be supported by this. For example, investigative work may require sudden, unexpected demands for equipment.
- Documentation – how will the short-term planning for equipment use be supported?

Selecting and Obtaining Resources

This is often best tackled when the science curriculum or individual topics are being revised. All the appropriate teachers can then be involved in helping to select the resources, which improves the likelihood of their being used appropriately. Details of equipment lists and evaluation checklists follow. Advance planning of topics in this way enables realistic budgets to be compiled, and can allow a longer-term strategy for the purchase of equipment. When money is limited, high priority items can be highlighted, and the remaining requirements provided over a period of years. One of the most difficult things to budget for is the replacement of worn-out and damaged equipment. Take a tip from industry where there is always a depreciation element (say 10%) in annual budget plans.

Materials and Equipment

Given the practical nature of investigative and experimental science, this is a key area of importance, and one which will consume most time, effort and money. Effective management by the co-ordinator can show very good returns in both staff morale and children's learning. There are a number of important sources of help and advice in this task, of which the most detailed is *Primary Science Equipment* by Rosemary Feasey (1998).

Choosing the Best Equipment

This is best tackled in topic-sized chunks, though often circumstances demand a more extensive search. In this *Primary Science Equipment* is very helpful. It provides an audit sheet and a full list of equipment, its likely cost and how to use it safely and with care. When considering particular types of resource, the CLEAPSS reports of good, value for money and safe equipment are invaluable. CLEAPSS publishes a termly newsletter for primary schools which provides updates, especially on safety issues. This lists all the equipment guides that are available. Both the newsletter and reports are free to members (see References and Further Reading.) Find out if your LEA is a member; most are. Another key publication is *Be Safe!* (ASE 1990) which includes lists of chemicals, electrical and heating equipment which is appropriate and safe for use in primary schools. There is sometimes no substitute in assessing equipment for getting your hands on it and the ASE Annual Meeting and many of the regional meetings give opportunities for this. Or you could invite the manufacturer to visit the school and give a demonstration.

How Much Will it Cost?

Unfortunately there is very little advice available on this key question, perhaps understandably, in the light of school's varying needs. ASE headquarters may be able to provide some information, and there are recommendations for secondary schools (Royal Society 1997). There are, however, ways in which costs can be reduced or money raised. You might consider the following:

- Local commerce, industry or community groups providing materials.
- Governors and parents appealed to for resources or money to purchase. But be specific or you may be given junk and fail to raise any money if the appeal is unattractive or misunderstood.
- Get a range of supplier's catalogues (see list in References and Further Reading) to compare prices. Some areas have bulk-buy outlets where materials, especially consumables, can be purchased much more cheaply than from conventional suppliers.
- For specialist equipment, such as microscopes, approach your local secondary school; you may be able to arrange a loan, or a visit, and at the least to try out their equipment and ask their advice.
- Keep a look out for educational competitions, grants and sponsorship opportunities – science and technology equipment often features in these. For example a recent reward from the Particle Physics and Astronomy Research Council (PPARC), included the provision of about £1000 of astronomy equipment to several schools.

Storage and Access

This is probably the most important aspect of managing resources in schools. The science co-ordinator needs to avoid becoming a science technician, for ever being badgered by staff about lost magnets or dead batteries. Involving staff in the planning of resource use can help in the sharing of this responsibility, whilst avoiding inconsistency in the use of equipment, in which the quality of children's learning opportunities can be damaged. Details of organisations will depend on curriculum objectives and the physical environment, but will probably include each of the following, to some extent:

- A central store for the more expensive and unusual equipment and perhaps topic-specific collections, under the direct control of the science co-ordinator, but with access for other staff.
- Classroom-based collections of everyday materials and collections, under the control of the teacher, perhaps with replenishment through the science co-ordinator.
- Access for children to most of the classroom resources, through activities which both develop their responsibility for materials and equipment, while ensuring their safety – and that of the equipment.
- A clear labelling and recording system which shows where an item is kept, when it is to be used, and how it is to be looked after, or replenished.

Primary Science Resources has a useful discussion of the advantages and limitations of various forms of storage, and of how responsibility can be shared.

People, Places and Living Things

These can all have key contributions to make to the quality of children's learning, but their use needs to be managed.

People

Visitors to the classroom can bring a reality to the topic being studied, for example a lighting engineer from a TV company. Many schools use medical experts to provide expertise in health topics. Another welcome addition is someone to assist in tutoring when investigations are being carried out. There are a number of sources of people:

- schemes run by educational institutions or the education branches of large companies
- health promotion organisations and educational charities
- parents and governors
- higher education institutions, through teacher training and research activities.

Places

There are many good reasons within science education, for taking children out of the classroom. But it always requires extra time, effort and possibly expense, so it is essential to plan in advance to ensure that best use is made of the visit, and that children are safe. Here are some ways that schools commonly use successfully:

- The school's own grounds can provide a fertile situation, not only for the natural environment, but also for looking at materials and studying forces and movement. Some schools are developing wildlife sanctuaries in their grounds with the help of the LEA or local environmental groups. Advice is also available from publications of environmental charities (see References and Further Reading). The process is an ideal way for children to learn about the relationships between humans and other living things, and to appreciate the need for a responsible attitude to the environment.

- Museums, interactive centres and the like usually arrange educational programmes based on their collections and are happy to discuss plans for visits. There are some interesting case studies of museum use in published form (South Eastern Museums Service, 1995). Reports of new developments and of teachers use of such visits can be found in the educational press, for example, ASE's *Primary Science Review* (e.g. Brooke and Solomon 1996, Neighbour 1997).

- Field trips are important for studies of special and different environments, and can provide formative experiences for children. Using recognised centres makes planning easier (see References and Further Reading) and advice is usually available locally, for example, through the LEA. *Be Safe!* Has useful guidance for ensuring that visits are accident free.

Living Things

This major area of scientific study poses particular resource issues; not least because of the need to ensure that things are always available in good condition!

Plants are relatively straightforward. There are of course issues about safe handling and of identifying poisonous plants. *Be Safe!* has a list of common ones and a safety code for using plants. Planning needs to take account of seasonal availability. There are guides available of suitable plants to grow in school classrooms, to supplement the ubiquitous bean and cress growing. *Be Safe!* has a short list.

Animals present more problems. There are laws protecting many wild species, others can be harmful to humans and all animals could be harmed by inappropriate use in the classroom. Guidance on what is allowed and what is suitable should be used in the planning. *Be Safe!* and a number of CLEAPSS guides are most useful (see References and Further Reading). In addition, LEAs will usually have policies which must be followed. Charities and other organisations concerned with animals produce their own advice and often provide suggested activities for classroom use. For example, the RSPCA published a collection of animal welfare activities, linked to the National Curriculum (RSPCA, 1996).

Micro-organisms are studied in junior classes, but only yeast and certain common moulds should be brought into the classroom. Growing micro-organisms is not appropriate in primary schools. The safety code in *Be Safe!* should be carefully followed.

Publications

These can serve several purposes in primary science. For teachers they give support to planning and to assessment, and give a wide range of ideas for activities and often some background science. For pupils there can be practical help in carrying out experimental procedures, reading and illustration for stimulus or revision, and opportunities to develop new ideas. The provision of text-based science for children helps to develop literacy and information handling skills.

Types of Publication

This range of purposes is reflected in the range of types of published resource (see Fig 4.3A).

Resource	Function	Examples of use
Children's information book or leaflet	For a stimulating context or detailed examples	Follow-up to teacher's overview of a topic, e.g. how animals adapt
Child's encyclopaedia	To teach info finding skill	Homework on a subject covered in class
Narrative writing	To engage in an imaginative way	By the teacher to introduce a topic
Work card or sheet	To provide detailed instructions	For a practical exercise (not an investigation)
Asssessment pack	To find out what has been learnt	For end of topic test
Planning guide to the curriculum	To assist schools in long and medium term	For key stage and topic planning
Topic activity packs	Indeas for classroom use	Planning lessons and schemes of work
Journal articles	To promote good teaching and learning	Could range from discussion of basic educational issues to ideas for classroom practice
Teaching schemes	Any of the above	All aspects

Fig 4.3A

With such a variety, and the competing claims of different publishers, it can be difficult to choose the best for one's own situation. Some teachers believe that only material they have developed for their own children will be suitable. However, it should be recognised that most published teaching resources are devised and written by experienced teachers and tried out with children. Many schools invest in a range of publications which can be adapted to support the planning, delivery and assessment of the curriculum in the way they require.

Choosing Publications

The science co-ordinator will need to take a lead in this but should involve all those who will use them, and the head teacher who will pay for them, if the selection is to be effective. There are several ways of going about this, some use could be made of the following:

- Follow the recommendations of colleagues in other schools and of advisers.
- Refer to reviews in the educational press, e.g. *The Times Educational Supplement, Primary Science Review*.
- Sift through publishers' catalogues, order inspection copies and sit down with the staff to evaluate.
- Use a checklist to identify needs and the evaluate the content of prospective solutions.

This checklist is based on the evaluations of teaching schemes by SCAA (1997).

1. What elements does the scheme contain and for what purposes? (See Fig 4.3A.)
2. How does the scheme cover and interpret the requirements of the National Curriculum or Curriculum Guidelines (Scotland)?
3. What advice and guidance is given in relation to assessment, in particular for investigative and experimental science?
4. How do the resources tackle progression and differentiation?
5. Is the material scientifically accurate?
6. Are the activities safe, and does the approach encourage pupils to take responsibility in this area?
7. Is the use of language in the pupil materials appropriate, and does it show progression?
8. Are the materials attractive and well-organised?
9. What is the scheme's overall fitness for purpose?

Such an analysis not only helps in the selection of the best resource for the school, it highlights areas in which the school will need to supplement or amend the scheme in use.

Media Resources

The range and availability of non-print media continues to grow rapidly. They offer new opportunities and particular problems in ensuring that their use enhances children's learning.

Information and Communication Technology (ICT)

This generally involves computer based devices and media such as disc-based software on floppies, CD-ROM or CDI, the internet and datalogging equipment such as environmental probes. These are covered in Chapter 3.8.

Radio and Audio Tapes

Audio resources can help children develop listening skills and encourage imaginative responses to narratives and fantasy. Their use in science is very limited and there are no broadcast programmes for schools in the subject, and very few tapes available.

Television and Videotapes

Television broadcasts are used regularly in over 90% of primary schools in the UK. With increasing availability of video recorders, this use is now mainly through prior recording so freeing use from broadcast schedules. In many cases the programmes are transmitted in batches at night so that schools can record series more conveniently. (If you can operate the video timer!) The educational broadcasters, BBC Education and Channel 4 Schools publish annual programmes with details of the programmes and of supporting publications. Broadcasts are often available subsequently as videotapes, and many other educational organisations also publish tapes, often as part of teaching packages. These are often available at below cost price because of sponsorship. Educational programmes differ from recreational TV and video in that they are designed for interactive use. The material may be presented in short sequences for ease of intervention, and the producers often publish guidance on how to use a programme or series. BBC and C4 each have a team of education officers whose job is to promote the effective use of the broadcasts.

Research studies have identified the main reasons given by teachers for using video as:

- the development of knowledge, skills and concepts
- the presentation of information in an interesting and stimulating way
- access to experiences which cannot easily be provided by the teacher
- to provide the teacher with additional expertise and ideas.

Television is an easy resource to use in most primary schools, but programmes still have to earn their place in the busy curriculum. The purpose above can be incorporated into a checklist for the effective use of video, for example:

1) Planning (during topic planning)
   - What aspects are best covered by video (e.g. for providing context or for prompting an investigation)?
   - What will be the aims in using a programme and what learning outcomes will be covered?
   - When will the programmes need recording?
   - Are there teacher's notes? When do they need ordering?

2) Selecting (in advance)
   - Is it age-appropriate?
   - Does the style fit in with the aims and learning outcomes (e.g. if it is to stimulate investigation it must leave questions unanswered)?
   - Will all of the programme be shown, and how?
   - Will the guidance notes be used and to what extent?

3) Preparing
- Has the physical environment been checked (i.e. equipment and viewing conditions)?
- Do children need 'warming up' to get the most out of the programme?

4) Viewing
- How will you check that children are attending to the programme?
- What questions can you ask at the conclusion of the viewing or each part of it?

5) Follow up
- What activities are to be carried out after the programme?
- What resources are needed for these?
- How will the learning outcomes be assessed?

About the Author

Martin Hollins is Senior Lecturer in Science Education at Roehampton Institute London, editor of Primary Science Review, and a freelance writer in science education.

References and Further Reading

ASE (1998) *Quality in Science Education*. Summary of Education Policies. ASE, Hatfield.

ASE (1990) *Be Safe!* Second Edition. ASE, Hatfield.

Brooke, H. and Solomon, J. (1996) Hands-on, brains-on: playing and learning in an interactive science centre. *Primary Science Review* No 44, pp 14–16.

Feasey, Rosemary (1998) *Primary Science Resources*. ASE, Hatfield.

Neighbour, Joanne (1997) *Primary Science Review,* No 46, pp 20–21.

OFSTED (1996) *Science and Mathematics in Schools.* HMSO, London.

SCAA (1997) *Analysis of educational resources in 1996/7 Key Stage 3 science schemes, Key Stage 2 mathematics schemes.* QCA Publications, London.

South Eastern Museums Service (1995) *Learning about science and technology in museums.* SEMS, London.

Royal Society (1997) *Science teaching resources: 11–16 year olds.* The Royal Society, London.

RSPCA (1996) *Animal welfare opportunities in the national curriculum.* RSPCA, Horsham.

Further Information

CLEAPSS School Science Service, Brunel University, Uxbridge UB8 3PH. Tel 01895 251496.

Reports include: *Small mammals, Plants for classrooms, Studying microorganisms in primary classrooms, Tadpoles* and *Safe use of household and other chemicals.*

Using the School Grounds

Learning through Landscapes, 3rd floor, Southside Offices, The Law Courts, Winchester SO23 9DL. Publishes *Growing with Trees* and other materials.

Tetra Pak has annual awards for Environmental Teaching in Primary schools. A booklet of winning ideas and details of the awards are available from Educational Communications, 50–54 Beak Street, London W1R 3DH. Tel 0171 453 4646.

Field Studies Organisations

Field Studies Council, Preston Montfort, Montfort Bridge, Shrewsbury SY41 1HW. Tel 01743 850674.

Royal Society for the Protection of Birds, The Lodge, Sandy, Beds SG19 2GL. Tel 01767 680551.

Educational Broadcasting

BBC Education Information, White City, London W12 7TS. Tel 0181 746 1111. Website http://www.bbc.co.uk/education/

Channel 4 Schools, PO Box 100, Warwick CV34 6TZ. Tel 01926 436444 and website www.channel4.com

4.4 Inspection and the Evaluation Cycle

David Oakley

Accountability has been the theme of much of the education legislation over the last ten years. Schools have been swamped by external imperatives, including inspection and national performance tables. A culture of measurement of attainment in order to raise standards has been generated by the school improvement and effectiveness movement. OFSTED inspection is the way which government has decided will most effectively guarantee schools' commitment to raising standards in England and Wales. The purpose of inspection is 'to identify strengths and weaknesses so that schools may improve the quality of education that they provide and raise the educational standards achieved by their pupils.' The inspection process is heavily focused on classroom practice. Documentation supporting the work of the school is analysed and judged in terms of its effectiveness in raising standards or maintaining high standards. Staff, particularly senior staff and co-ordinators, are interviewed about their roles. Parents are canvassed on their view of the school by questionnaire and at a meeting. After inspection, the feedback and report are intended to give direction to the school's strategy for planning, review and improvement by an evaluation that is rigorous and identifies key issues for action.

This chapter outlines perspectives before, during and after an inspection. It is useful to visualise the process as an evaluation cycle:

- Pre-inspection – what have we achieved so far and where are we going?
- Inspection – external evaluation snapshot, where we are now.
- Post-inspection – what has been achieved and what do we need to do next?

Although the *context* for discussion is the practice in England and Wales, the *principles* of planning and evaluation apply across the UK.

Background and National Perspective

Until September 1993 external evaluation of schools in England and Wales was largely the province of HMI. As there was only ever a maximum number of 500 HMI to cover all areas of curriculum and management, their visits for survey purposes or as part of general inspections were on a very long cycle – 20 to 50 years! Local Education Authority advisers worked with schools in a variety of ways, including subject reviews, but these visits were seldom in the inspection mode. The rationale for advisers' visits to schools varied and criteria were rarely shared with schools. This changed in 1993 with the establishment of OFSTED and the recruitment of thousands of inspectors. LEA advisers metamorphosed into inspectors and the OFSTED culture became a fact of life.

OFSTED Inspection, School Monitoring and Self-evaluation

The function of OFSTED inspection is threefold:

- To provide information to parents. (OFSTED was set up as part of the first plank of the Parents' Charter.)
- To provide data for the national picture.
- To raise standards and help schools to improve.

Schools share with OFSTED the third aim. Strategies to enable departments and schools to monitor and evaluate themselves are an essential part of the repertoire of an effective school. The purpose of monitoring is to provide information about practice. It is the gathering of information and evidence, followed by the sifting, sorting, classifying, analysing and generally making sense of the information and evidence collected. Evaluation is about identifying strengths and weaknesses, finding out if stable systems need to change or whether changes have been effective, drawing conclusions, making value judgements and proposing improvements. The endorsement of successful strategies is not precluded! The process provides a firm basis for accountability and confirms that intentions have been translated into action. OFSTED criteria provide a suitable agenda on which schools can base their own criteria and superimpose their own priorities. The criteria for teaching, for example, are fundamental to any examination of the quality of teaching taking place. Any external monitoring is very orientated towards these criteria. Accountability is on the political agenda for the foreseeable future.

From February 1998 schools have had data about their performance from OFSTED statistics which compare a school's performance in the national curriculum tests with the national average and against those of similar schools. Schools are grouped on the basis of the proportion of pupils eligible for free school meals as an index of disadvantage. QCA provide these benchmark figures. Schools are also rated against others with similar intakes under the headings 'Standards Achieved by Pupils' and 'Quality of Education'. The ratings are reached by taking assessments from the reports prepared during OFSTED inspections. Schools are given one of four grades, ranging from 'very good' to 'substantial improvement required'.

Measuring Attainment – Where Are We Now?

Any strategy for improvement must be a continuous one, but as schools come up for re-inspection the need to check out how well they are on target is particularly vital. The key features looked at by inspectors are performance indicators – the measurable outcomes of pupils' attainment and progress.

Collection and management of data is a relatively new responsibility for primary co-ordinators, but they need:

- Baseline information.
- KS1 teacher assessment.
- KS2 test results and teacher assessment for science.
- Any interim optional QCA interim tests results.

Middle schools may have to deal with mid key stage transfer and adopt their own strategies for assessing their intake and output.

The data needs to be collected on an annual basis and displayed in a graphical or tabular form that conveys the pattern of attainment of the pupils in the subject. Computer software enables data to be manipulated in seemingly infinite ways. It is important not to be seduced by the technology; the audience must always be the focus. Is the school communicating with parents, LEA inspectors, OFSTED inspectors or the local press? Is a bar chart, pie chart, 3-D histogram or line graph appropriate? Trends are vitally important in the analysis of data. The three-year rolling average of results is probably the most important data to be communicated. This technique irons out the fluctuations in annual performance. It is important to set annual targets that are realistic and take into account previous performance. A commentary should summarise the analysis of the data, explaining trends and deviations and should be accompanied by analysis of strategies adopted as a consequence of previous analysis and evaluation.

Comparisons can be made by adding other sets of information, e.g. KS2 data on entry with the data on Y6 national test results or the relative performance of boys and girls. This is particularly useful in value added analyses (see Chapter 3.2), though care must be taken not to include too much data at a time.

Collection of data is a vital part of the target setting. Targets for particular key stages must be realistic and based upon information about the particular cohort. Evidence from any generic testing undertaken by the school can be used to supplement subject data. Historical trends may give a false picture on occasion, but effective record keeping and comparison with previous year groups enable attainable targets to be set.

Checking Other Aspects of Provision

Indicators of other achievements may be less easy to evaluate. How well science education is meeting the success criteria set out in the subject development plan and action plan from the previous inspection is part of the scheduled review process. Though the timing of an inspection may result in some aspects of review being brought forward, schools should not feel that they must be deflected from their own review priorities. Part of inspection is to evaluate the effectiveness of the school's systems and processes and as schools will only have 10 to 13 weeks notice of an inspection, any pre-inspection check will rely heavily on the review cycle already in place. Any progress check the science co-ordinator may wish to make on classroom practice should supplement the routine monitoring that is taking place. The monitor/evaluate/review cycle is a way of managing improvement through self-evaluation of effectiveness. The basic principle of monitoring and evaluation is to be clear about the purpose. In order to make the process manageable within the extensive repertoire of a department it must be realistic in the demands made on teachers' time. An OFSTED inspection, thorough and rigorous though it may be, still only provides a snapshot. The true picture unfolds on a daily basis. Monitoring can be 'soft' and informal including occasional visits to a colleague's classroom or informal conversations about how 'things are going'. It is difficult to use such evidence as part of a structured approach and informality may lead to individuals feeling threatened if attempts are made to use observations of these sorts.

Formal monitoring needs to be part of a planned and agreed process, which involves as many colleagues as possible in achieving the desired aims.

The sequence is to:

- Identify the subject of the monitoring as part of the development plan cycle or action planning in response to an inspection or other external review.
- List the criteria for the monitoring.
- Decide upon the strategy to be adopted.
- Decide who will be involved and the time scale.
- Decide on how and to whom the findings are to be reported.

The subject of monitoring will depend upon development priorities and where the school is in the OFSTED cycle or other review (e.g. LEA) cycle. Unforeseen national directives may require action planning. Monitoring of policies should be done routinely on a fairly long cycle over several years, though some such as assessment may need more frequent checking. It is very important that policies are dated and the next review is also identified.

Approaches to monitoring can involve:

- Lesson observations.
- Sampling of pupils' exercise books or other work.
- Questionnaires.
- Self-monitoring.

Essential to each of these is a checklist, taken off the OFSTED shelf or devised by the team or an individual. Criteria for classroom observation would probably be best based on the OFSTED criteria but could be focused on differentiation or assessment. In practice few schools have the luxury of time to carry out this exercise. In the schools where it does happen, it is usually part of senior management's monitoring role.

The sampling of pupils' work is probably the easiest way into monitoring. Small numbers of pupils' books across a year group can provide a representative range of evidence quickly and the task can be shared so that everyone is both monitor and 'monitee'!

For example, adherence to the marking and assessment policy can be checked:

- Is assessment used formatively to improve pupils' learning?
- Are the specified grades for effort and attainment actually used?
- Is marking correct, accurate and consistent?
- Does the marking of homework reflect the effort that pupils have put into it?
- Are there positive comments?
- Are comments to complete missing work followed up?
- Is the balance of comments about understanding to those about presentation appropriate?

Monitoring of marking is probably the most important routine monitoring activity and should result in improved feedback to pupils about their progress. Examples of good marking, which helps pupils to know how to improve should be photocopied as part of the science marking policy in order to share good practice. (See also Chapter 3.2.)

The second most important routine monitoring activity is the checking of the delivery of the scheme of work. It is probably best to separate the two activities, but both could be covered as part of the same exercise. The following questions might be useful:

- Is the scheme being properly covered in terms of content and level specified?
- Is the variety of teaching and learning approaches specified by the scheme being delivered?
- Are the recommended worksheets being selected?
- Is work being matched to the abilities of pupils in the class, with different work set?
- Is the work sufficiently challenging?
- Is the scheme itself sufficiently detailed?
- Would aspects benefit from review?
- Does the response of pupils indicate that they are interested in their work and motivated by it?
- Are pupils making appropriate progress through the topic and longer term?

Feedback can be generic and minuted as part of subject meetings. For example:

- "Most of us are not using the extension suggestions in the two-lesson block on magnetism."
- "Most of us did not give the pupils an opportunity to investigate their own ideas in AT1 in this topic."
- "Few of the special needs worksheets we bought for the scheme are being used."

Improvement of the effectiveness of the scheme of work is a tangible outcome of monitoring and evaluation. Schemes of work are probably always going to be under review. Another way of monitoring the performance of the scheme of work is to analyse the results of any testing of pupils that takes place. It may be that pupils are consistently performing badly in one topic, not because of the intrinsic difficulty of the topic but because of the way in which it is being taught and a revision of the scheme might be in order.

If monitoring is not part of established practice, a pupils' work scrutiny is the quickest way of checking how policies and the scheme of work are being implemented. A sample from each class to include two high-attaining, two average-attaining and two low-attaining pupils' work can provide information on how effectively science teaching matches up with documented intentions. The response to the findings should be the subject of an action plan designed to improve any shortcomings by identifying, for example, in-service training, policy reviews or resource requirements.

Evaluation

Once data and other information have been organised strategic planning is the next stage. Many schools churn out data without much in the way of analysis, particularly of successful strategies. Why were the results so good that year? What did we do that we can replicate to repeat that success? The same is true of the findings of monitoring. It is the evaluation stage that is crucial in identifying strategies needed, or existing successful. The relative performance of boys and girls is a case in point. To simply produce an analysis which says that boys outperform girls at KS2 and by how much is seldom accompanied by a list of strategies designed to raise the attainment of girls and subsequent evaluation of these strategies.

Analysis of the success of strategies should be based on both measurable indicators of success, such as test results, and intuitive evaluations. 'Gut reactions' can be just as important as statistics for something as personal as interaction with pupils. Professional experience is often underrated in the current vogue for quantification. What are the elements in improving attainment in science? The most important is the will to improve. Strategies need to be seen as positive rather than defensive. The ambition for perceptible, specific improvements needs to be realistic, based on a sound knowledge about what is and what is not currently being achieved. Promotion of self-esteem should not just be an aim for pupils' development, but also for the effective functioning of staff. Strategies should be reinforced by the sharing of vision and goals. Success should be celebrated with colleagues, pupils, senior managers, parents and governors. Rigour and pace are vital aspects of the process. The key to realistic pacing of raising standards initiatives is the subject development plan. (See Chapters 3.2, 4.1 and 4.2.)

The Inspection

The subject teaching during the inspection week needs to be planned well ahead so that the variety of work going on represents the full repertoire of the school. During the inspection week exemplify the good practice you seek to demonstrate throughout the year.

Good practice means:

- Act and teach as you do on a good day!
- Make sure that you have planned the whole week thoroughly and that you share the purpose and aims of each lesson with pupils.
- Allow time for end-of-lesson review with pupils.
- Ensure that all the resources that you need are to hand.
- Make sure that any classroom support staff know what is expected of them.
- Leave your planning out for inspectors to read, include background information about pupils on the special needs register.
- Have somewhere available for the inspector to sit.
- Check the learning environment for tidiness, range of resources, range of pupils' work on display.
- Make sure that work is marked up-to-date.
- Keep as far as possible to your prepared timetable and make sure that sessions start and end on time.

Post-inspection – Action Planning

Post-inspection an action plan needs to be devised to deal with issues raised by the inspection. There may well be an overlap with the subject development plan, but the issues in an action plan are specific to an inspection report or to deal with issues identified as a priority by the school. An action plan is normally devised when there is a need to bring about fairly rapid changes. It needs to include:

- The issue to be addressed.
- Actions planned.
- Time scales.
- Responsibilities for leading.
- Responsibilities for monitoring.
- Training required.
- Resource implications and costing (including time).
- Success indicators.
- Date of review.

The cycle of monitoring and evaluation begins again, with the progress of the action plan being the focus. Action plan issues usually become incorporated into subject development plans. It is important for the purpose of reporting on progress during future inspections that the action plan retains a life of its own, running alongside the development plan.

Future Directions

The current OFSTED guidance is already well honed and the subject of major revision. Fundamental changes in the near future are unlikely. HMCI Chris Woodhead has acknowledged that schools are moving towards self-evaluation, but still considers that the external check is an essential part of the process of school evaluation and improvement. More radical models for inspection still involve external evaluation/accreditation of schools' own work. In September 1997 re-inspection of secondary schools began, primary and special re-inspection followed in September 1998. The focus in the second, six-year phase is on how the school in general has improved or maintained high standards and how subjects, particularly core subjects, have moved on. The first report and the school's response to it through the action plan will be the starting point. External monitoring by the LEA required by the 1998 Education Act will also be considered, as will the results of the school's own monitoring. The re-inspection phase presents schools with an opportunity to show how they have tackled the subject issues raised by their first inspection in the intervening period and what systems they have in place to support improvement. The systems in place for science within the school must constantly be stimulated by reference to national initiatives. Keeping up with what is new in science needs to complement introspection. Networking is vital. Schools need new ideas. Awareness of new commercial schemes, research evidence, projects aimed at raising standards, new equipment, the latest revision guides, software, ideas for science clubs and visits, is part of creating an ethos of excitement, enjoyment and improvement.

About the Author

David Oakley taught science for 20 years in grammar and comprehensive schools and a tertiary college before becoming an advisory teacher then inspector for science in Dudley LEA. A past chair of the National Science Advisers and Inspection Group, he has been an OFSTED Registered Inspector since OFSTED inspections began in 1993.

References and Further Reading

Barber, M., Stoll, L., Mortimore, P. and Hillman, J. (1995) *Governing Bodies and Effective Schools,* London, DFE.

OFSTED (1994) *Improving Schools*, London, OFSTED.

OFSTED (1995) *The OFSTED Handbook, Guidance on the Inspection of Schools,* London, HMSO.

OFSTED (1998) *Standards and Quality in Education 1996/7. The Annual Report of Her Majesty's Chief Inspector of Schools*, London, The Stationery Office.

OFSTED (1995) *Planning Improvement :Schools' Post-inspection Action Plans,* London, HMSO.

White, P. and Poster, C. (Eds) (1997) *The Self-monitoring Primary School*, London and New York, Routledge.

Kent Consultants and Teacher's Digest (1997) *Journal of Raising Achievement in Science*, by subscription from Kent Consultants.

Index